Investigations

CPO Focus on

Life
Science

An Integrated Middle School Series

cpo science

cpo science

A member of
School Specialty
Science

CPO Focus on Life Science Investigations
First Edition
Copyright © 2007 Delta Education LLC, a member of the School Specialty Family
ISBN-10: 1-58892-255-3
ISBN-13: 978-1-58892-255-7
3 4 5 6 7 8 9 - QWE - 11 10 09 08 07

CPO Science

80 Northwest Boulevard

Nashua, NH 03063

(866)588-6951

http://www. cposcience.com

Printed and Bound in the United States of America

Scott Eddleman - Author

B.S., Biology, Southern Illinois University; M.Ed., Harvard University

Taught for 13 years in urban and rural settings. Developed two successful science-based school-to-career programs. Nationally recognized teacher trainer in inquiry-based and project-based instruction. Participated in a fellowship at Brown University where he conducted research on the coral reefs of Belize. Worked on National Science Foundation-funded projects at TERC. Scott has been a principal writer and curriculum developer for CPO Science for the last six years.

Mary Jo Carabatsos Ph.D. - Principal Writer and Content Editor

Ph.D., in Cell, Molecular and Developmental Biology from Tufts School of Medicine

Taught High School Biology and Physical Science for the last 4 years. Prior to teaching, she worked as a research scientist. Mary Jo advises, edits material and writes investigations.

Erik Benton - Principal Investigation Editor

B.F.A., University of Massachusetts

Taught for 8 years in public and private schools, focusing on inquiry and experiential learning.

Kristen Dolcimascolo - Principal Writer

B.A. Biology from the University of Delaware

Taught middle school science for the past 6 years. She has also taught middle school math. Currently teaching 7th grade at Wayland Middle School in Massachusetts.

Tom Hsu, Ph.D - Principal Writer

Ph.D. Massachusetts Institute of Technology

Nationally recognized innovator in science and math education and the founder of CPO Science.

SENIOR EDITOR

Lynda Pennell - Executive Vice President

B.A., English, M.Ed., Administration, Reading Disabilities, Northeastern University; CAGS Media, University of Massachusetts, Boston

Nationally known in high school restructuring and for integrating academic and career education. Served as the director of an urban school for 5 years and has 17 years teaching/administrative experience. in the Boston Public Schools. Lynda has led the development for CPO Science for the last six years.

EDITORIAL CONSULTANTS

Christine Golden

Chris has been the Project Manger for *Imperial Communications* since 1999 and in the publishing business for 22 years. She is now managing editor and owner of *Big Dog Publishing* Services. Christine's work centers around the editing of K-12 textbook materials.

CONTRIBUTORS

Kelly A. Story - Reviewer

B.S., in Chemistry and English from Gordon College and a Masters in Chemistry from the University of Massachusetts Lowell

Kelly has taught chemistry and is currently a Lab Instructor at Gordon College, MA .

Laine Ives - Writer

B.A., from Gordon College and graduate coursework at Cornell University's Shoals Marine Laboratory and Wheelock College

Laine has taught high school English overseas and environmental education at a middle school in New England. Laine has developed CPO products for the past five years.

Jill Elenbaas - Reviewer

B.A., in Biology and Environmental Science from Bowdoin College in Maine

She is currently teaching eighth grade Earth Science in Wayland. MA and has teaching experience as a seventh grade Life Science teacher in Dedham, MA.

Mary Beth Abel Hughes – Writer

B.S., Marine Biology, College of Charleston; M.S., Biological Sciences, University of Rhode Island

Mary Beth taught science and math at an innovative high school. She has expertise in scientific research and inquiry-based teaching methods. She has been a principal writer at CPO since 2000.

REVIEWERS

Nancy Joplin
English Language Arts Department Chair
Ray Wiltsey Middle School, CA

Jodye Selco Ph.D.
Professor, Center for Education and Equity in Math, Science and Technology
California State Polytechnic University, Pomona

Brian E. Goodrow
Physical Science Teacher
Apple Valley Middle School, CA

Philip L. Hunter
Science Department Chair
Johnson Middle School, CA

Bianca N. McRae
Science Teacher, Department Chair
Menifee Valley Middle School, CA

Tia L. Shields
Seventh Grade Life Science/Health and English
Language Learning Teacher
Nicolas Junior High School, CA

Kelly McAllister
Science Teacher
Gage Middle School, CA

Brad Joplin
Eighth Grade Science Teacher
Ray Wiltsey Middle School, CA

Tony Heinzman
Teacher
Apple Valley, CA

Sylvia Gutman
Science Teacher/Department Head
David A Brown Middle School
Lake Elsinore Unified School District, CA

ILLUSTRATION/DESIGN

Polly Crisman -Designer and Illustrator
B.F.A., University of New Hampshire
Graphic artist with expertise in advertising and marketing design, freelance illustrating, and caricature art.

Bruce Holloway - Cover Designs
Pratt Institute, N.Y.; Boston Museum School of Fine Arts
Expertise in product design, advertising, and three dimensional exhibit design. Commissioned for the New Hampshire Duck Stamp for 1999 and 2003.

Jesse Van Valkenburgh - Designer and Illustrator
Graduated from the Rochester Institute of Technology with a B.A. Illustration
Jesse has worked at PC Connection as a graphic designer for catalog and direct mailing design, logo design, as well as some illustration work. He has also has experience in creative design and film production.

James Travers - Graphic designer and animator
Associate's Degree of Applied Business and Commercial Art, Akron University
Jim has held positions as graphic designer, art development manager, and currently is a commissioned artist.

EQUIPMENT DESIGN

Thomas Narro - Senior Vice President

B.S., Mechanical engineering, Rensselaer Polytechnic Institute

Accomplished design and manufacturing engineer; experienced consultant in corporate reengineering and industrial-environmental acoustics.

Danielle Dzurik

B.S., Industrial Design, Auburn University

Danielle is responsible for helping to develop new products and improve upon older designs.

Thomas C. Hsu, Ph.D

Ph.D. in Applied Plasma Physics from the Massachusetts Institute of Technology

He is a nationally recognized innovator in science and math education and the founder of CPO Science. Well known as a consultant, workshop leader and developer of curriculum and equipment for inquiry based learning in science and math.

MATERIAL SUPPORT

Kathryn Gavin - Purchasing and Quality Control Manager

Kathryn is responsible for all functions related to purchasing raw materials and quality control of finished goods. She works closely with product development and design.

Michael Grady - Technical Service Coordinator

Associate's degree, Berklee College of Music

Michael has 10 years experience in the related customer service fields. Michael has a varied personal background and holds an Associates Degree in Arranging and Performing from the Berklee College of Music and a Medical Technician Diploma from Middlesex Community College. He works with product development and design to ensure customer quality.

Lisa LaChance - Senior Materials Specialist

Associate's of Science in Accounting

Lisa evaluates material samples to ensure materials meet project requirements. She develops and manages the release of materials specifications.

TECHNICAL SUPPORT

Tracy Morrow

B.A., English, Texas A&M University; M.A., English, Sam Houston State University, TX

Tracy taught middle school in Klein ISD, a suburb of Houston, Texas, for 9 years preparatory and English at Tomball College for 5 years. Tracy worked as a technical writer in the oil and gas, airlines, and real estate industries. Currently she offers consulting services and technical training. Tracy's expertise lies in the editing program Framemaker.

How to Read an Investigation

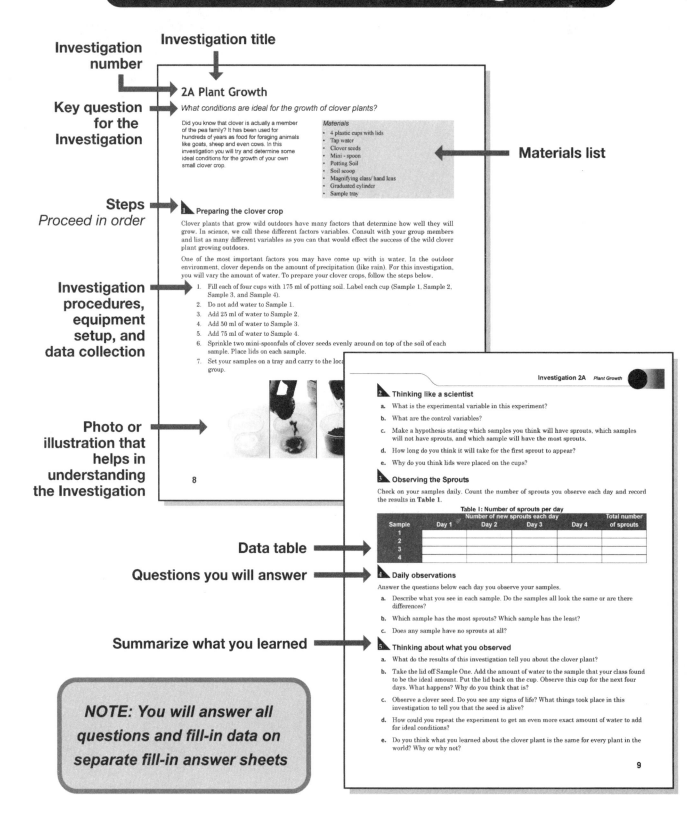

Investigation number

Investigation title

Key question for the Investigation

Materials list

Steps *Proceed in order*

Investigation procedures, equipment setup, and data collection

Photo or illustration that helps in understanding the Investigation

Data table

Questions you will answer

Summarize what you learned

2A Plant Growth

What conditions are ideal for the growth of clover plants?

Did you know that clover is actually a member of the pea family? It has been used for hundreds of years as food for foraging animals like goats, sheep and even cows. In this investigation you will try and determine some ideal conditions for the growth of your own small clover crop.

Materials
- 4 plastic cups with lids
- Tap water
- Clover seeds
- Mini - spoon
- Potting Soil
- Soil scoop
- Magnifying glass/ hand lens
- Graduated cylinder
- Sample tray

1. Preparing the clover crop

Clover plants that grow wild outdoors have many factors that determine how well they will grow. In science, we call these different factors variables. Consult with your group members and list as many different variables as you can that would effect the success of the wild clover plant growing outdoors.

One of the most important factors you may have come up with is water. In the outdoor environment, clover depends on the amount of precipitation (like rain). For this investigation, you will vary the amount of water. To prepare your clover crops, follow the steps below.

1. Fill each of four cups with 175 ml of potting soil. Label each cup (Sample 1, Sample 2, Sample 3, and Sample 4).
2. Do not add water to Sample 1.
3. Add 25 ml of water to Sample 2.
4. Add 50 ml of water to Sample 3.
5. Add 75 ml of water to Sample 4.
6. Sprinkle two mini-spoonfuls of clover seeds evenly around on top of the soil of each sample. Place lids on each sample.
7. Set your samples on a tray and carry to the loca... group.

8

Investigation 2A *Plant Growth*

2. Thinking like a scientist

a. What is the experimental variable in this experiment?

b. What are the control variables?

c. Make a hypothesis stating which samples you think will have sprouts, which samples will not have sprouts, and which sample will have the most sprouts.

d. How long do you think it will take for the first sprout to appear?

e. Why do you think lids were placed on the cups?

3. Observing the Sprouts

Check on your samples daily. Count the number of sprouts you observe each day and record the results in **Table 1**.

Table 1: Number of sprouts per day

| Sample | Number of new sprouts each day | | | | Total number of sprouts |
	Day 1	Day 2	Day 3	Day 4	
1					
2					
3					
4					

4. Daily observations

Answer the questions below each day you observe your samples.

a. Describe what you see in each sample. Do the samples all look the same or are there differences?

b. Which sample has the most sprouts? Which sample has the least?

c. Does any sample have no sprouts at all?

5. Thinking about what you observed

a. What do the results of this investigation tell you about the clover plant?

b. Take the lid off Sample One. Add the amount of water to the sample that your class found to be the ideal amount. Put the lid back on the cup. Observe this cup for the next four days. What happens? Why do you think that is?

c. Observe a clover seed. Do you see any signs of life? What things took place in this investigation to tell you that the seed is alive?

d. How could you repeat the experiment to get an even more exact amount of water to add for ideal conditions?

e. Do you think what you learned about the clover plant is the same for every plant in the world? Why or why not?

9

NOTE: You will answer all questions and fill-in data on separate fill-in answer sheets

Table of Contents

Lab Skills and Equipment Setups

1A Measurement and Data

Is there a relationship between human wingspan and height?

Birds have a wingspan. To measure it, scientists spread the bird's wings and measure from the tip of one wing, to the tip of the other wing.

You also have a wingspan. Stretch your arms apart in front of you. Your wingspan is the measurement from fingertip to fingertip. In this investigation, you will look for a relationship between human wingspan and height. You will then choose another set of human dimensions to compare and look for relationships. In the process, you will learn to make accurate measurements.

Materials
- Metric tape measure
- Pencil
- Graph paper

 Measuring wingspan and height

1. You will work with a lab partner. Have your partner spread his/her arms out straight from the shoulders on each side of the body as shown below.
2. *Estimate* your partner's wingspan, in centimeters. Record your estimate in Table 1.
3. Using a metric tape measure, measure the distance in **centimeters** from the tip of the longest finger on one of your partner's hands to the tip of the longest finger on the other hand. This is the wingspan. Your measurement should be to the nearest millimeter (the smallest divisions on the tape measure). Enter the measurement in Table 1.
4. Have your partner remove her/his shoes. *Estimate* your partner's height in centimeters. Record your estimate in Table 1.

5. Measure your partner's height from the bottom of the heel to the top of the head. Record the data in Table 1.

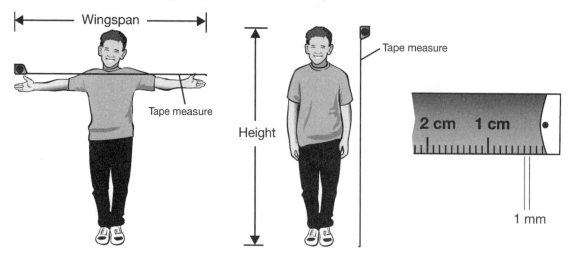

Table 1: Wingspan and height for you and your partner

	Wingspan (*estimate* - cm)	Wingspan (*actual* - cm)	Difference (larger value minus smaller value)
Lab partner			
You			
	Height (*estimate* in cm)	Height (*actual* in cm)	Difference (larger value minus smaller value)
Lab partner			
You			

 Stop and think

a. Why are centimeters better for measuring human wingspan and height than meters?

b. Look at the difference between your estimate and the actual measurements (the last column in Table 1). Did the difference get lower as you took more measurements? Explain these results.

c. Based on the results of your measurements, do you think there is a relationship between human wingspan and height? If so, what do you think it is? State your answer in the form of a hypothesis.

Gathering class data

1. Record your data (actual measurements only) on the board in front of the classroom.
2. Once the class data table is complete, copy the data into Table 2.
3. Complete Table 2 by finding the difference between wingspan and height for each row. Subtract the lesser amount from the greater amount to find the difference.
4. Look at the data in Table 2. Do the data support your hypothesis? Explain.
5. After reading Section 1.3 in your text, make a graph of the data in Table 2. Plot wingspan on the *x*-axis and height on the *y*-axis. Can you identify a relationship on the graph? Why is a graph a better way to look at the data?

Table 2: Class data

Student	Wingspan (cm)	Height (cm)	Difference

On your own

a. Take measurements of wingspan and height for 10 people outside of your classroom. Create your own data table and graph.

b. Is your data consistent with your class data? What can you conclude from your results?

1B Variables in an Experiment

How do scientists conduct a good experiment?

Imagine a jumping frog trying to escape from a predator. The frog needs to get the greatest distance out of each jump. What variables affect how far the frog will travel? What about the angle at which the frog aims when it jumps? How do you think the launch angle will affect the distance the frog will travel? In this Investigation, you will try launching *marbles* (not frogs!) at different angles in order to find out how launch angle affects distance traveled. As a result, you'll learn how to conduct a good experiment.

Materials

- Marble launcher
- Plastic marbles
- Tape
- Metric tape measure
- Graph paper
- Ruler

Safety Notes:

- **Never launch marbles at people.**

- **Wear safety glasses or other eye protection when launching marbles.**

- **Launch only the black plastic marbles that come with the marble launcher.**

1 ▶ Setting up

1. Identify the parts of the marble launcher.

2. For this experiment, you will use the fifth slot of the barrel to launch the marble for each trial. Pull the launch lever back and slip it sideways into the fifth slot. Put a marble in the end of the barrel. The marble launcher is now ready to launch.

3. You will change the angle for each launch starting at 10 degrees and increasing 5 degrees up to 80 degrees.

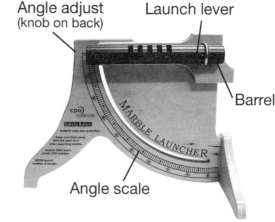

4. A minimum of two people are needed per launcher. One person releases the launch lever and the other watches where the marble lands. A few launches should be done at each angle to be sure that the data is accurate. It also takes a few times to accurately find the spot where the marble lands.

5. Use a strip of masking tape on the floor to make sure that the marble launcher is set back in the same place every time. A tape measure laid along the floor provides a good way to measure the distance traveled by the marble.

2 ▲ Stop and think

a. At which angle do you think the marble will travel the greatest distance? State your answer to the question as a <u>hypothesis</u>.

b. What is the <u>experimental variable</u> in this experiment? What are the <u>control variables</u>?

c. Why is it important to make a few practice launches at each angle?

3 ▲ Doing the experiment

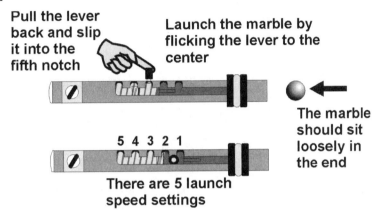

In the table below record your two best trials for each launch angle:

Table I: Launch angle and distance data

Launch angle (degrees)	Distance (meters)	Distance (meters)	Launch angle (degrees)	Distance (meters)	Distance (meters)
10			50		
15			55		
20			60		
25			65		
30			70		
35			75		
40			80		
45			85		

4 Analyzing your data

a. There is an angle at which the marble launcher will cause the marble to travel the farthest. The angle may not be obvious from the data you have collected. Graphs help scientists to organize data into patterns that are easier to see. For graphing purposes, which variable is the _independent variable_? Which is the _dependent variable_?

b. Make a line graph showing how the distance changes with the launch angle. Plot the independent variable on the *x*-axis and dependent variable on the *y*-axis.

c. Look at your graph. At what angle does the marble attain the greatest distance?

d. You are challenged to launch a marble to travel a distance of 4.00 meters. At what angle will you set the launcher?

e. Referring to your answer for question (d), state another angle that would give you the same result.

f. Is the 4.00 meter distance the only distance that you can reach using two different angles? State three other distances and the angles you would use to reach that distance.

g. Explain why two angles can be used to reach the same distance.

h. Write a paragraph about a situation in which it would be better to use one angle rather than the other.

5 Designing your own experiment

a. Besides launch angle, which other variables can you change on the marble launcher?

b. Choose a different variable you can change. Write a question you have about how that variable affects another variable.

c. State your hypothesis to the question.

d. Design an experiment to test your hypothesis. List the materials and procedures for your experiment, then get approval from your teacher.

e. Conduct your experiment. Be sure to make a good data table before you begin. Get approval from your teacher for your data table design.

f. Make a graph of your data and analyze your results.

g. State a conclusion to your experiment. Did your results support your hypothesis? If so, explain why. If not, explain how you would change your hypothesis or experiment.

h. Present your findings to the class.

2A Plant Growth

What conditions are ideal for the growth of clover plants?

Did you know that clover is actually a member of the pea family? It has been used for hundreds of years as food for foraging animals like goats, sheep and even cows. In this investigation you will try and determine some ideal conditions for the growth of your own small clover crop.

Materials

- 4 plastic cups with lids
- Tap water
- Clover seeds
- Mini - spoon
- Potting soil
- Soil scoop
- Magnifying glass/ hand lens
- Graduated cylinder
- Sample tray

 Preparing the clover crop

Clover plants that grow wild outdoors have many factors that determine how well they will grow. In science, we call these different factors <u>*variables*</u>. Consult with your group members and list as many different variables as you can that would affect the success of the wild clover plant growing outdoors.

One of the most important variables you may have come up with is water. In the outdoor environment, clover growth depends on the amount of precipitation (like rain). For this investigation, you will vary the amount of water. To prepare your clover crops, follow the steps below.

1. Fill each of four cups with 175 mL of potting soil. Label each cup (Sample 1, Sample 2, Sample 3, and Sample 4).
2. Do not add water to Sample 1.
3. Add 25 mL of water to Sample 2.
4. Add 50 mL of water to Sample 3.
5. Add 75 mL of water to Sample 4.
6. Sprinkle two mini-spoonfuls of clover seeds evenly around on top of the soil of each sample. Place lids on each sample.

7. Set your samples on a tray and carry to the location your teacher designates for your group.

 Thinking like a scientist

a. What is the experimental variable in this experiment?

b. What are the control variables?

c. Make a hypothesis stating which samples you think will have sprouts, which samples will not have sprouts, and which sample will have the most sprouts.

d. How long do you think it will take for the first sprout to appear?

e. Why do you think lids were placed on the cups?

 Observing the sprouts

Check on your samples daily. Count the number of sprouts you observe each day and record the results in **Table 1**.

Table 1: Number of sprouts per day

Sample	Number of new sprouts each day				Total number of sprouts
	Day 1	Day 2	Day 3	Day 4	
1					
2					
3					
4					

 Daily observations

Answer the questions below each day you observe your samples.

a. Describe what you see in each sample. Do the samples all look the same or are there differences?

b. Which sample has the most sprouts? Which sample has the least?

c. Does any sample have no sprouts at all?

5 ▲ Thinking about what you observed

a. What do the results of this investigation tell you about the clover plant?

b. Take the lid off Sample One. Add the amount of water to the sample that your class found to be the ideal amount. Put the lid back on the cup. Observe this cup for the next four days. What happens? Why do you think that is?

c. Observe a clover seed. Do you see any signs of life? What things took place in this investigation to tell you that the seed is alive?

d. How could you repeat the experiment to get an even more exact amount of water to add for ideal conditions?

e. Do you think what you learned about the clover plant is the same for every plant in the world? Why or why not?

2B Brine Shrimp

What conditions are ideal for the growth of brine shrimp?

Brine shrimp are crustaceans that live in salty bodies of water like The Great Salt Lake in Utah, estuaries, and brackish ponds. These different bodies of water can have different amounts of salt in them. In the first part of this investigation you will to hatch some brine shrimp in four different samples of water. Each sample will have a different amount of salt in it. Over the course of the next few days you will check your four different samples of water to see how many brine shrimp have hatched. They are very small, but you will be able to see them and even count them if you look very closely.

Materials

- 4 plastic cups with lids
- Aged tap water (2 liters)
- Brine shrimp eggs
- Mini - spoon
- Sea salt or Kosher salt
- Salt scoop
- Magnifying glass/ hand lens
- Microscope
- Graduated beaker
- Sample tray

WARNING — This lab contains chemicals that may be harmful if misused. Read cautions on individual containers carefully. Not to be used by children except under adult supervision.

 Preparing the samples

1. From your 2 liters of water, measure out 150 mL of water into the graduated beaker.
2. Fill one of your four plastic cups up with the water. Mark this cup "Sample One".
3. Fill and label the other three samples with 150 mL of water each.

Now that you have four samples of water, you need to decide how much salt to put into each sample. One sample should contain no salt at all. Many times scientists change the variables in their experiments in even amounts. Decide how many scoops of salt you want to increase each sample by, like two scoops each time. For example:

- Sample one - zero scoops
- Sample two - two scoops
- Sample three - four scoops
- Sample four - six scoops

Use even, level scoops when you add salt to a sample. Label how many scoops go into each sample on the lid of each cup. Once the samples have been labeled, calculate the parts per thousand concentration of salt in each. To do this, follow the directions on the next page.

To do this, measure the mass of one scoop with a balance. The number of scoops in your sample times the mass of one scoop of salt is the mass of salt in each sample. Calculate the number of grams of salt for each sample and record the information in **Table 1** to calculate the parts per thousand of salt in each sample. There are 1000 grams of water in a liter, so to find the parts per thousand of salt in the water.

$$\frac{\text{number of grams of salt}}{150 \text{ mL of water}} \times \frac{1000 \text{ mL of water}}{1000 \text{ grams of water}} = \frac{\text{number of grams of salt}}{1000 \text{ grams of water}}$$

Table 1: Salt concentration

Sample number	Grams of salt (no. of scoops x mass of 1 scoop)	Parts per thousand

2 ▲ Thinking like a scientist

a. What is the experimental variable in this experiment?

b. What are the control variables?

c. What do you think will happen when the eggs are added to the samples?

d. Which sample do you think will have the most shrimp in two days?

e. Which sample do you think will have the fewest shrimp in two days?

f. Do you think the sample with no scoops of salt added will have any shrimp in two days? Why or why not?

3 ▲ Hatching the shrimp

Now that you have your samples prepared it is time to add the shrimp eggs. Each sample should have the same size mini-spoonful of eggs in it.

1. Add one mini-spoonful to each sample. (Even though it is very small, one mini-spoonful is plenty of eggs to hatch a whole colony in each sample!)

2. Put the cover on each sample and set the cups into the sample tray.

3. Make sure all samples are properly labeled and capped.

4. Store the samples in a place that will have light for at least part of the day, like a classroom.

4 Observing the results

Carefully look at each of your samples. What do you see?

Record your observations every 24 hours in your notebook:

a. Describe what you see in each sample.

b. Do the samples all look the same or are there differences?

c. Which sample has the most brine shrimp and which has the least?

d. Are there any other observations you have made?

5 Thinking about what you observed

a. What does this part of the investigation tell you about the ideal level of salt the brine shrimp need to thrive?

b. Why is it useful to include a sample that has no salt added to it?

c. If some shrimp hatched in a sample of water that had no salt added, what would that tell you about that sample of water?

d. Compare your results to the results of all the groups in your class. Overall, what seems to be the best salt concentration for hatching brine shrimp?

e. How could you modify the experiment to get a more precise ideal salt concentration for hatching brine shrimp?

6 Preparing Samples for Investigation 3B

For Investigation 3B you will need to have four identical samples ready to begin the experiment. This means you will need to hatch the brine shrimp ahead of time.

1. Measure 150 mL of water each for four samples. Use the same sized cups that you used from **Part 1** of this investigation.
2. Your class came up with an ideal amount of salt for the brine shrimp. Add this amount of salt to each sample.
3. Add one mini-spoonful of brine shrimp eggs to each sample.

This will give you four identically prepared samples for Investigation 3B. Put a lid on each sample, write the names of your group members on a piece of paper and place the samples on the paper as you set them aside in the place your teacher has assigned. Your samples will be ready for Investigation 3B.

3A Living Conditions

How will similar populations react to different variables?

There are many variables that affect plants as they grow. Clover plants are no exception. Plants have been able to grow in almost every environment on the planet, even under water. Each environment has a wide range of conditions that can affect a plant's success and health. We will test living conditions that may affect clover plants in this investigation.

Materials

- 4 sample clover populations
- 4 different sized containers
- 4 lids
- sand
- dirt
- potting soil
- Plant Grow light
- fertilizer
- Graduated cylinder
- measuring spoon/cup

WARNING — This lab contains chemicals that may be harmful if misused. Read cautions on individual containers carefully. Not to be used by children except under adult supervision.

1 ▶ Conditions to be tested

Since there are so many variables influence plants growth, each group in your class will select one to test. Some variables may take longer than others to show a noticeable effect on the clover plants. The list below shows the different variables your group can test.

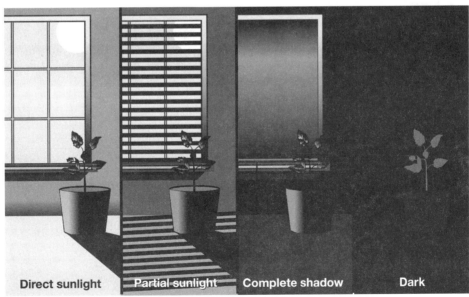

Direct sunlight   Partial sunlight   Complete shadow   Dark

1. Light levels - dark, shade, window, direct sunlight
2. Varying amounts of fertilizer.
3. Different types/brands of fertilizer
4. Comparing kinds of soil, dirt, sand, or a combination of these

Once you have decided with your group which variable you are going to test, prepare your experiment setups. Prepare setups with different levels of the variable you are testing. One of your setups should be the control group. The _control group_ is the experiment that is set up under "normal" conditions. For example, if you are testing light levels, your control group would be the one placed in lighting conditions the plant would normally encounter.

2 ▲ Thinking like a scientist

a. What is the experimental variable in your experiment?

b. What are the control variables?

c. What question are you asking with your experiment?

d. Based on your experimental variable, what is your hypothesis?

e. What is the purpose of testing the effect of varying a condition on both clover plants from seed and existing sprout populations?

f. How will you set up your control group? Explain why it is your control group.

g. How long do you think it will take for the first effects to be observable?

h. Sketch your experiment set-up. Label parts.

3 ▲ Observing the populations

Now that you have your samples prepared, it is time to look for any effects that the varying conditions may have on your populations. Check on your samples daily and record your group's observations in **Table 1**.

Table 1: Plant population data

Sample	Effect on populations			
	Day 1	Day 2	Day 3	Day 4
1				
2				
3				
4				

4 ▲ Observing the results

Carefully look at each of your samples. Try not to disturb the ongoing experiment while observing your samples. What do you observe?

In 24 hours:

a. Describe what you observe for each sample.

b. Do the samples all look the same or are there differences?

c. Which sample seems most affected by the varying condition? The least affected?

Answer questions a-c for each of the four days.

5 Thinking about what you observed

a. What do the results of this investigation tell you about the variable you tested?

b. Do the results support your hypothesis?

c. How could you repeat the experiment to get an even more exact result on the effect of your experimental variable?

d. Do you think the variable you tested has the same effect on every other organism on Earth? Why or why not?

e. Can you set up an environment for a clover crop that combines all of the most successful conditions observed by each group in your class? Try it out and see what happens.

6 Presenting what you have learned

Work with your group to come up with a presentation that clearly explains what you have learned. All members of the group should be involved in some way. You can use these points as a guideline to make your presentation;

1. State the question your experiment was asking.
2. State your hypothesis.
3. Explain the setup and procedure of your experiment.
4. Give an overview of the data you collected, pointing out any trends or patterns you observed.
5. State your conclusion (does your data support your hypothesis?) and propose an alternative conclusion if one is possible.

3B Testing Pollutants

How will similar populations react to different pollutants?

Human activities affect ecosystems in both positive and negative ways. One negative effect is pollution. A *pollutant* is a variable that causes harm to an organism. Pollutants enter ecosystems naturally and through human activities. For example, volcanic eruptions are a natural source of sulfur dioxide. Coal-burning power plants are a human source of this pollutant. In this investigation you will test the effect of different levels of several pollutants on identical brine shrimp populations.

Materials

- 4 sample brine shrimp populations
- rubbing alcohol
- milk
- hydrogen peroxide
- sugar solution
- unknown solution
- yeast solution
- vinegar
- ammonia solution
- plastic droppers
- Microscope/magnifying glass
- Slides, depression slides, coverslips
- Beaker
- measuring spoon/cup

WARNING — This lab contains chemicals that may be harmful if misused. Read cautions on individual containers carefully. Not to be used by children except under adult supervision.

 1 Population to be tested

By using four identical containers with about the same number of brine shrimp, you will have four similar populations that can be tested for their tolerance to a particular pollutant. Each group will test the effect of one pollutant and try to find an acceptable level (if any) that will not seriously harm a brine shrimp population.

1. Once your group has chosen a pollutant, decide how many drops will be added to each cup. Check with your teacher once you have agreed on an amount.

2. Label one of your containers "Sample 1 - Control Group." You will not add any pollutants to your control group.

3. Add the first amount of pollutant to another sample and label it "Sample 2." Be sure to label your pollutant and how much was added to each population.

4. Repeat step 3 for your other two samples, and be sure to label the pollutant and the total amount added to the population.

Sample 1 — CONTROL GROUP Sample 2 — 20 mL Sample 3 — 40 mL Sample 4 — 60 mL

2 ▶ Thinking like a scientist

a. What is the experimental variable in this experiment?

b. What are the control variables?

c. Do you think all four samples be affected? If not, which ones will and which ones will not?

d. Why is it important to add no pollutant to the control group?

e. How long do you think it will take for the first effects to be observable?

f. Why was it important to use the same sized containers with the same number of brine shrimp in each population?

3 ▶ Observing the populations

Now that you have your samples prepared, it is time to look for any effects that the pollutants may have on your populations. It is important to make sure all four samples are stored in conditions that are as similar as possible. Check on your samples daily and record your group's observations in **Table 1**.

Table 1: Brine shrimp population observations

Sample	Effect on populations			
	Day 1	Day 2	Day 3	Day 4
1				
2				
3				
4				

4 ▶ Observing the results

Examine a few brine shrimp from each sample each day with a magnifying glass or microscope and slides. Note any physical effects or changes caused by the pollutant and record your observations.

a. Describe what you see in each sample.

b. Do the samples all look the same or are there differences?

c. Which sample seems most affected by the pollutant?

d. Which sample is the least affected?

e. Does there seem to be an amount that does not affect the population?

Answer questions a-e for each of the four days.

Thinking about what you observed

a. What do the results of this investigation tell you about the pollutant you tested?

b. Did you observe any physical effects or changes when you observed your brine shrimp closely?

c. How could you modify the experiment to get a more precise amount for your acceptable pollutant level?

d. Do you think the pollutant you tested has the same effect on every other organism on Earth? Why or why not?

e. How can acceptable levels of a pollutant be determined for a particular environment?

f. How do you think scientists determine acceptable levels of pollutants for humans?

4A Reflection and Refraction

What is the difference between reflection and refraction?

Looking in a mirror, we see a twin of ourselves reversed left-to-right. A fish underwater appears in a different place from where the fish really is. Both of these illusions are caused by the bending of light rays. This Investigation explores reflection and refraction, two processes that bend light rays.

Materials

- Light and Optics kit
- Drop of milk
- Protractor & metric ruler
- Clear plastic cup
- Water

1 ▸ Observing the law of reflection

Setting up

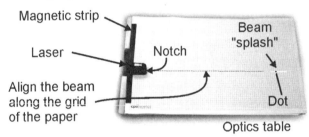

Reflecting the beam

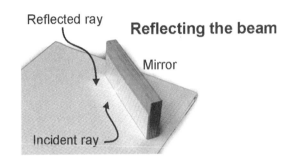

1. Set a sheet of graph paper on the optics table.
2. Connect the laser and put it on the optics table so that the base is tipped up on the magnetic strip.
3. Align the laser so the beam points down slightly and follows one horizontal line across the paper.
4. Draw a dot about 1/3 of the way along the beam "splash" on the graph paper.
5. Set the mirror on the optics table so its shiny front surface is on the dot and draw a line on the graph paper marking the front face of the mirror.
6. Use a pencil to mark the light rays going toward and away from the mirror.
7. Change the graph paper and repeat parts 1-3 with the mirror set at 3-4 different angles.

2 ▸ Thinking about what you observed

A diagram showing how light rays travel is called a *ray diagram*. Lines and arrows on a ray diagram represent rays of light.

Drawing the ray diagram

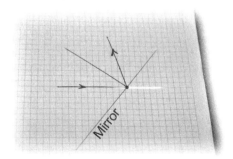

a. Draw a ray diagram showing the surface of the mirror and the light rays before and after the mirror.

b. Which is the incident ray? Label it on your ray diagram.

c. Which is the reflected ray? Label it on your ray diagram.

3 ▸ The law of reflection

a. For each ray diagram, draw a line perpendicular to the mirror surface at the point where the rays hit. This line is called the _normal line_.

b. Use a protractor to measure the angle between the normal and the incident and reflected rays.

c. Write down your own statement of the law of reflection, describing the relationship between the angles you measured.

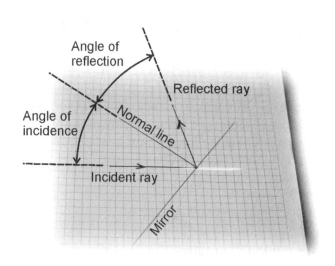

Table 1: Angles of incidence and reflection

	Diagram #1	Diagram #2	Diagram #3	Diagram #4
Angle of incidence				
Angle of reflection				

4 ▸ Light rays going through a prism

A prism is a solid piece of glass with polished surfaces. Prisms are useful for investigating how light bends when it crosses from one material to another, such as from air into glass or glass into air.

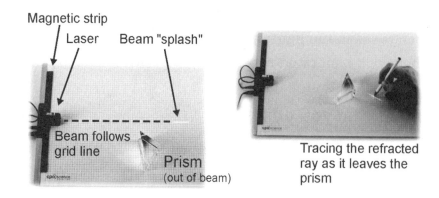

1. Set the laser on the optics table so that the base is tipped up on the magnetic strip. The beam should make an extended splash along the graph paper.
2. Set the prism into the laser beam so the beam comes out the opposite short side (diagram).
3. Rotate the prism in the beam and observe where the beam comes out.

Sketching what you observed

a. Draw at least one ray diagram showing a laser beam that is refracted passing through the prism. The *refracted ray* is the ray that comes out of the prism.

b. Draw a ray diagram showing a laser beam that is reflected passing through the prism.

c. Draw a ray diagram showing a laser beam that is both refracted and reflected passing through the prism.

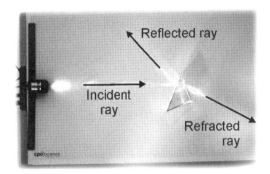

 Seeing reflection and refraction at the same time

Both refraction and reflection often occur when light hits a boundary between materials such as the boundary between glass and air. The amount of light reflected or refracted depends on the angle at which you are looking relative to the surface.

 Fold a paper card marked with A and B

The image in the prism changes as you move your head!

1. Take a piece of graph paper about the size of a business card and draw a line about 5 centimeters from one edge, dividing the rectangle in half. Draw the letter A on one side of the line and the letter B on the other side.

2. Fold the paper on the line and wrap it around one of the corners of the prism that is not a right angle.

3. Look into the prism. Move your head up and down to change the angle at which you look.

 Thinking about what you observed

a. Draw a diagram showing the path of the light when you see the letter A.

b. Draw a diagram showing the path of the light when you see the letter B.

c. Is the image in the prism always reflected or refracted or can there be both reflection and refraction at the same time?

8 ► The angle of refraction

The milk makes the beam visible passing through the water.

Using an index card to locate and mark the center of the beam.

1. Fill a clear plastic cup about 1/2 with water. Add one drop (only one!) of milk to the water in the cup.

2. Set the cup on the optics table on a fresh sheet of graph paper. Use a pencil to trace around the base of the cup.

3. Shine the laser beam through the cup so it passes off-center. Use an index card to find and mark the laser beam going into and out of the cup.

4. Remove the cup and draw the ray diagram.

9 ► Thinking about what you observed

The change in direction of a refracted ray depends on the angle with the normal line.

a. Draw the normal line to the surface at the points where the light ray enters and leaves the cup. A round cup is convenient because the normal line points toward the center of the circle.

b. When the light is going from air into water does the ray bend toward or away from the normal?

c. When the light is going from water back into air does the ray bend toward or away from the normal?

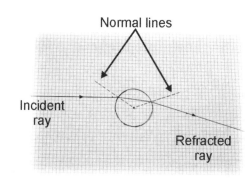

4B The Microscope

How does a microscope create an image?

The microscope is an important tool used in many branches of science to examine small objects and fine detail. In this investigation we will look at how a microscope works.

Materials
• Microscope
• Metric ruler
• Light & Optics kit
• Prepared *Hydra* slide
• Graph paper

1 **Finding the magnification of a lens**

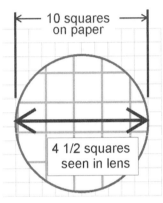

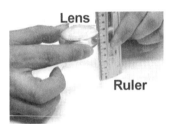

Measuring the distance from the lens to the paper

1. Take one of the lenses and set it on a piece of graph paper. Count the number of unmagnified squares that cross the diameter of the lens. In the example, the lens is 10 squares wide.

2. Look at the graph paper through the lens held above the paper at different distances. Move the lens until you have the biggest squares you can see clearly in the lens.

3. Count the number of magnified squares that cross the diameter of the lens. For example, the picture shows 4 1/2 squares across the lens.

4. The magnification is the number of unmagnified squares divided by the number of magnified squares. In the example, there are 10 unmagnified squares and 4.5 magnified squares. The magnification is 10 ÷ 4.5, or 2.22.

5. Try the experiment again using a ruler to measure the distance between the lens and the paper. Notice that the magnification changes with different distances.

Table 1: Magnification data for a single lens

	Distance to paper (cm)	# of squares on the graph paper (unmagnified squares)	# of squares in the lens (magnified squares)	Magnification
White Lens				
Black lens				

Thinking about what you observed

a. Is the image in a magnifying glass inverted or upright?

b. At what distances will the lens act like a magnifying glass? What happens when the object is more than a focal length away?

c. Describe something that looks completely different under a magnifying glass than when seen with the un-aided eye.

 Using a microscope

The microscope is an optical instrument used to look at very small things. The concepts of reflection, refraction, image formation, and magnification all come together in the microscope

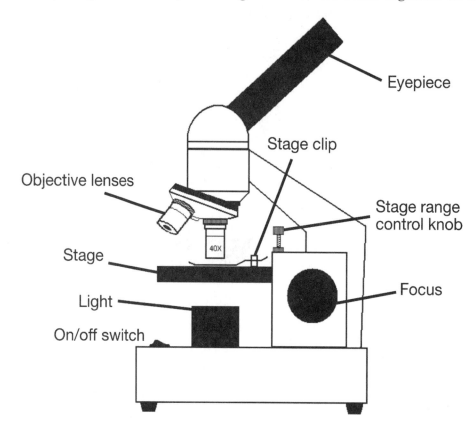

1. Look at the *Hydra* slide with your naked eye and draw a picture of what you see.
2. Select the 4x objective lens on your microscope.
3. Place the *Hydra* slide on the stage and secure it with the slide clamps.
4. Look through the eyepiece and use the focus knob to get a clear image. Does this look different than what you expected? Sketch what you see.

5. When you are done with the 4X objective lens, use the 10X and the 40X objective lenses. Make sketches of what you observe in the circles below.

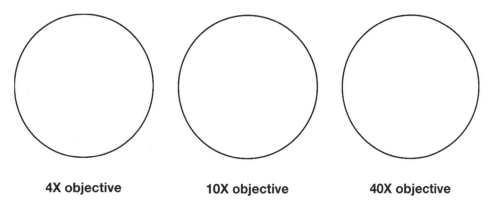

4X objective   **10X objective**   **40X objective**

 Microscope optics

When you look through a microscope the light that leaves the object on the slide goes through a series of lenses and even a prism on its way to your eye. Look at the light ray diagram for your microscope. Light passes through an objective lens, a field lens, a prism, and an eyepiece.

a. In which parts is refraction taking place?

b. In which parts is reflection taking place?

c. Set up the Hydra slide with the 4X objective lens and bring it into focus. Is the image you see in the microscope right side up or inverted compared to the hydra on the slide?

d. Move the slide left and right on the stage and observe how the image in the microscope moves. What part do you think causes this?

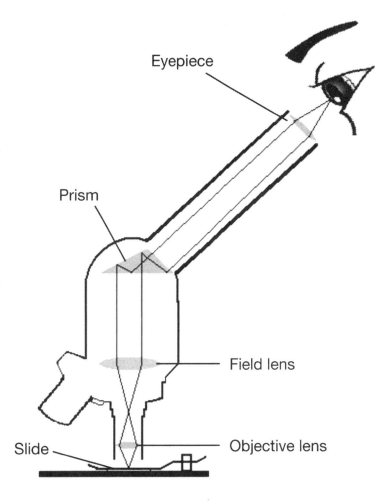

5. Microscope magnification

There are three objective lenses on your microscope. Each one has a label on it that describes its "power", which is how much magnification it provides. There is one more part that helps magnify what you see; the eyepiece.

a. Look on the side of the eyepiece of your microscope. What is its power?

b. The total magnification of the image is the product of the objective lens power and the eyepiece power. What are the three possible total magnifications available with your microscope?

Table 2: Microscope magnification

Objective lens power		Eyepiece power		Total image magnification
	X		=	
	X		=	
	X		=	

c. CHALLENGE! Bring the *Hydra* slide into focus with the 4X objective lens. Measure the distance from the end of the objective lens to the slide. Switch to the 10X objective lens bring the image into focus and measure the new distance. How do the 4X and 10X distances compare, and what does that tell you about their focal lengths? Make a prediction about how the 40X lens will compare with the other lenses and check your prediction. What did you find?

5A Examining Onion Tissue

What is onion tissue made of?

Do you think peeling an onion will make you cry? Well, here's your chance to test your hypothesis. In this investigation, you will peel a thin layer from a piece of onion. You will stain that layer of tissue on a microscope slide. Then you will examine your slide under a microscope and make sketches of what you see.

Materials

- Microscope
- Slides
- Coverslips
- Tweezers
- Piece of onion
- Iodine stain

Safety tip: Wear gloves, goggles, and an apron while preparing the slides.

WARNING — This lab contains chemicals that may be harmful if misused. Read cautions on individual containers carefully. Not to be used by children except under adult supervision.

 1 Preparing a slide of onion tissue

Onions have many layers. The inner surface of each layer has a thin layer of tissue that's easy to peel off. Since it is almost transparent, you will need to apply a stain so you can see things under a microscope. Follow the procedures below to make a slide of onion tissue.

1. Place a drop of iodine stain onto a slide.
2. Using the tweezers, gently peel the thin layer of tissue off the inside of a small piece of onion.
3. Using the tweezers, gently lower the onion skin onto the slide. Be careful not to crease the skin.
4. Use the tweezers to place a cover slip over the onion skin.

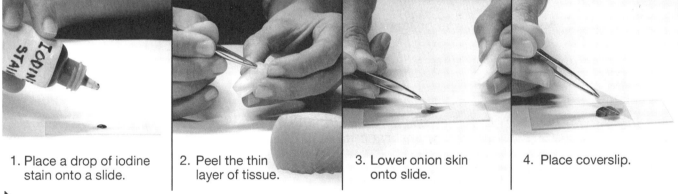

1. Place a drop of iodine stain onto a slide.

2. Peel the thin layer of tissue.

3. Lower onion skin onto slide.

4. Place coverslip.

2 Stop and think

a. What is the purpose of the iodine stain?

b. What do you think you will see under the microscope? In your notebook, sketch what you think you will see.

c. What is a tissue? What is the next level of organization above tissues? What is the level of organization below tissues?

3 **Observing onion tissue under a microscope**

1. Lower the stage on your microscope to its lowest point.
2. Switch to the low power objective lens.
3. Place your slide on the stage and secure it with the clips.
4. Bring the slide into focus with the knob.
5. Make a detailed sketch of what you see in the spaces provided. Record your observations.
6. Lower the stage and switch to medium power and repeat steps 4 and 5.
7. Lower the stage and switch to high power and repeat steps 4 and 5.

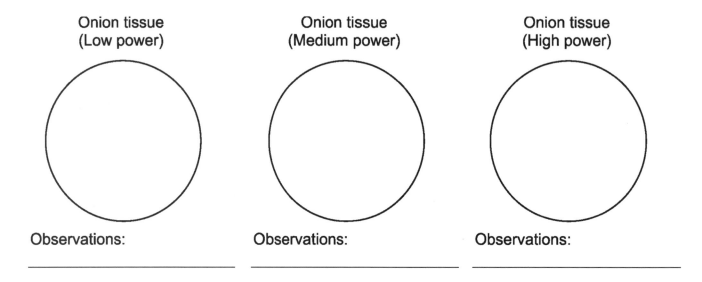

Onion tissue (Low power)

Onion tissue (Medium power)

Onion tissue (High power)

Observations:

_____

_____

Observations:

_____

_____

Observations:

_____

_____

 4 **Thinking about what you observed**

a. Based on your sketches and observations, what is onion tissue made of?

b. How many individual square structures could you see under low power? Medium power? High power?

c. How can you tell where one square structure ends and another begins? What do each of the individual structures you observed have in common?

d. When Robert Hooke looked at cork under a microscope in 1663, he called each of the square structures a *cell* because they reminded him of tiny rooms. Do your observations of onion cells agree with his? Explain why or why not.

e. Look at the diagram of a plant cell in Chapter 5 of your textbook. Which structures can you identify in your onion cells? Label them on your sketches.

5B Animal and Plant Cells

What are the differences between animal and plant cells?

In this investigation you will compare animal cells (your own epithelial cells and prepared slides) and plant cells (live Ulothrix - an algae that is closely related to plants, and the onion cells you observed in the last investigation).

Materials
- Microscope
- Slides
- Coverslips
- Tweezers
- Flat toothpicks
- Prepared slide of muscle tissue
- Live *Ulothrix*
- Methylene blue stain

Safety tip: Wear gloves, goggles, and an apron when preparing slides.

WARNING — This lab contains chemicals that may be harmful if misused. Read cautions on individual containers carefully. Not to be used by children except under adult supervision.

 Observing animal cells

The cells that line the inside of your mouth are called *epithelial cells*. These cells are easy to collect and observe. Follow the procedures below.

1. Place a small drop of methylene blue stain onto a clean slide.
2. Remove a clean flat toothpick. Wet the wide end of the toothpick using tap water.
3. Gently scrape the inside of your cheek with the wide end of the toothpick. DO NOT USE FORCE!
4. Place the toothpick into the stain on the slide and gently swirl to mix the cheek cells with the stain. Dispose of the toothpick as directed by your teacher. DO NOT REUSE THE TOOTHPICK.
5. Using tweezers, gently place a coverslip on top of the methylene blue solution as shown.
6. Place the slide on the microscope stage and observe under low power, medium power, and high power. Sketch what you see and record your observations in Table 1.
7. Dispose of the cheek cell slide as directed by your teacher.
8. Obtain a prepared slide of muscle tissue cells. Place the slide on the microscope stage and observe under low power, medium power and high power. Sketch what you see and record your observations in Table 1.

1. Place a drop of stain on slide.
2. Wet wide end of a flat toothpick.
3. GENTLY scrub the inside of your cheek. *DO NOT SCRAPE WITH FORCE!*
4. Swirl toothpick in stain. Dispose of toothpick as directed.
5. Lower coverslip onto slide.

Table 1: Animal cell sketches and observations

Cheek cell (4X)	Cheek cell (10X)	Cheek cell (40X)
Observations:	Observations:	Observations:
Muscle tissue (4X)	**Muscle tissue (10X)**	**Muscle tissue (40X)**
Observations:	Observations:	Observations:

2 ◢ Thinking about what you observed

a. What is the purpose of adding methylene blue to the cheek cells?

b. How are the cheek and muscle cells different? How are they similar?

c. Look at the diagram of an animal cell in Chapter 5 of your textbook. Which organelle was most prominent when looking at cheek cells under the microscope?

d. How many individual cheek cells could you see under low power? Medium power? High power?

e. Identify the nucleus, cell membrane, and cytoplasm in one of the cheek cells under high power. Label them on your sketch.

f. How many individual muscle cells could you see under low power? Medium power? High power?

g. Identify and label the nucleus and cell membrane in a muscle cell. Label them on your sketch.

3 Observing Ulothrix cells

1. Place a drop of water onto a clean slide.
2. Place some Ulothrix filaments into the drop of water.
3. Using tweezers, gently place a coverslip onto the filaments.
4. Examine the Ulothrix under low, medium, and high power.
5. Sketch what you see and record your observations in Table 2.

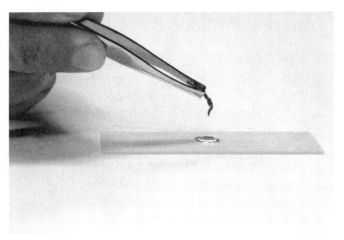

Table 2: Ulothrix cell sketches and observations

Ulothrix cells (4X)	Ulothrix cells (10X)	Ulothrix cells (40X)
Observations:	Observations:	Observations:

4 Thinking about what you observed

a. In Investigation 5A, you needed a stain to observe onion cells. Why didn't you need a stain to observe the Ulothrix cells?

b. Look at the diagram of a plant cell in Chapter 5 of your textbook. Which organelles can you identify in the Ulothrix cell slide?

c. How are the Ulothrix cells similar to the onion cells you observed in Investigation 5A? How are they different?

d. Label the following on your high power sketch of Ulothrix cells: nucleus, cell wall, cytoplasm, vacuole, chloroplasts.

5 Applying your knowledge

a. Based on your sketches and observations, what are the structures that animal and plant cells have in common?

b. Based on your sketches and observations, what are the structures found only in plant cells?

6A Diffusion and Osmosis

How does water move into and out of a cell?

Water passes into and out of the cell by osmosis. *Osmosis* is the diffusion of water across a membrane from an area of higher water concentration to an area of lower water concentration. In this investigation, you will use an egg membrane as a model system and observe the effects of water movement when the egg is placed in different solutions.

Materials

- 600 mL beakers/clear plastic cups (2)
- Wax pencil/permanent marker
- Balance
- Vinegar
- Tablespoon
- Fresh eggs (2)
- 50 mL beakers/plastic cups
- Paper plates
- Distilled water
- Corn syrup

WARNING — This lab contains chemicals that may be harmful if misused. Read cautions on individual containers carefully. Not to be used by children except under adult supervision.

 Dissolving the eggshell

1. Obtain two 600-mL beakers. Number them "Egg #1" and " Egg #2." Write your initials or group number on each beaker.

2. Obtain two eggs. Measure the mass of one of the eggs and place it into the beaker labeled Egg #1. Record your results in the first column of Table 1.

3. Repeat with the next egg and place it in the beaker labeled Egg #2. Record your results in the first column of Table 1.

Table I: Egg mass data

	Raw Egg	Vinegar (after 24 hours)	Water or Syrup (after 24 hours)
Egg #1			
Egg #2			

4. Pour 200 mL of vinegar into each beaker.

5. Record observations in Table 2, and place the two beakers in a safe place overnight.

Table 2: Egg experiment observations

	Day	Observations
Egg #1	1	
Egg #2	1	
Egg #1	2	
Egg #2	2	
Egg #1	3	
Egg #2	3	

6. Observe the eggs the next day, and record your observations in Table 2.

7. Slowly pour the vinegar out of each beaker. Be very careful not to rupture the egg cell membrane.

8. Carefully remove the egg using the tablespoon, **rinse with water**, and place each egg on its own labeled paper plate.

9. Measure the mass of each egg.

10. Record this information in the second column of Table 2.

2 ▸ Stop and think

a. What was the effect of placing both eggs into vinegar overnight?

b. What happened to the mass of each egg after being placed into vinegar overnight? Use what you know about osmosis and diffusion to explain the results.

c. If you think of the egg as a "cell," what does the fluid inside of the egg represent? What does the membrane that surrounds the cell represent?

d. In the next part of the investigation, you will place Egg #1 into a beaker containing distilled water and Egg #2 into a beaker containing corn syrup. Based on what you know, what do you think will happen to the mass of the egg when placed in distilled water overnight? In corn syrup overnight?

3 ▸ Placing the eggs into different solutions

1. Return the eggs to their respective beakers.

2. Pour distilled water into the Egg #1 beaker until the egg is completely covered.

3. Pour corn syrup into the Egg #2 beaker until the egg is completely covered. *If the egg floats, place a cup with water on top of the egg to keep it submerged.*

4. Place the two beakers in a safe place overnight.

5. After 24 hours, observe each egg, and record your observations in Table 2.

6. Slowly pour the water and syrup out of the respective beaker. Be very careful not to rupture the egg membrane.

7. Carefully remove the egg using the tablespoon, **rinse with water**, and place each egg on its own labeled paper plate.

8. Measure the mass of each egg.

9. Record this information in the third column of Table 1.

10. Return the eggs to their respective beakers, and wait for your teacher to collect them.

4 Thinking about what you observed

a. In the Stop and think section above (question d), you were asked to predict what would happen to each egg in the experiment. How did your results compare with your prediction?

b. Which beaker contained a greater concentration of water compared with the concentration of water in the egg, the one labeled Egg #1 or the one labeled Egg #2?

c. After 24 hours, did Egg #1 contain more, less, or the same amount of water as it did before the experiment? What is your evidence?

d. After 24 hours, did Egg #2 contain more, less, or the same amount of water as it did before the experiment? What is your evidence?

e. Use the terms *concentration, osmosis, diffusion* to explain why water moved *into* one egg and *out* of the other.

5 Exploring on your own

a. What would happen if you left the eggs in water and syrup for a longer period of time (another day, for example)? Is it possible to return the eggs to their original state before placing them into distilled water or corn syrup?

b. What would happen if you placed the egg originally in corn syrup (Egg #2) into distilled water? Could you restore the egg to its original state?

c. What would happen if you placed the egg originally in water (Egg #1) into syrup? Would it shrink? Try it.

6B Photosynthesis and Color

Does the color of light affect photosynthesis?

Living organisms, both plant and animal, contain chemicals known as *pigments*. A pigment's color is determined by the wavelengths of light that the pigment reflects. Plant leaves contain *chlorophyll*, a pigment that is vital to photosynthesis. In this investigation we will find out which colors of light are needed by chlorophyll to sustain photosynthesis.

> **Materials**
> * Four small potted plants
> * Plant grow light (75 W)
> * Red light (75 W)
> * Blue light (75 W)
> * Green light (75 W)
> * Four light fixtures
> * Water
> * Thermometer

 Setting up

Plants use sunlight in their natural habitat to produce energy through the process of photosynthesis. Sunlight is a pure white light, made up of all the colors together. What do you think would happen to plants if we didn't use white light, but instead used individual colors of light?

1. Find a place in your classroom where you can set up the four lights and four small potted plants. You may need to place small cardboard dividers between the plants to make sure only the specific color of light you want falls on each plant.

2. Label each plant with the color of light. All of your plants should be in similar condition and approximately the same size.

3. Once the plant/light set up is in place, put a thermometer in one of the plant areas to monitor temperature. You won't keep track of the temperature, but you will check it periodically to make sure the plants don't get too hot. This may harm them and spoil the experiment.

Stop and think

a. What is the experimental variable in this experiment?

b. What are the control variables?

c. Make a hypothesis stating how you think the color of light used will effect each plant. Think about the color of your plant. What color or colors is it reflecting? What colors or colors is it absorbing?

 Doing the experiment

1. The experiment begins when the lights are turned on. Discuss with your teacher if you will be using a 12-hour timer to turn the lights on or off, if this will be done manually, or if they will be on 24 hours a day.
2. Decide with your group if and/or how you want to water your plants.
3. Check on your plants each day and record your observations in your journal. Use a data table like Table 1 below to record your observations. Include a column to describe the initial condition of your plants.

Table 1: Plant growth/health data

Day ___		
Color	Initial condition	Change in condition
Grow light		
Red		
Green		
Blue		

 Thinking about what you observed

a. What color is your plant? If that particular color is getting to your eyes from the plant, is the plant reflecting or absorbing that color?

b. What is the plant doing with the colors it absorbs?

c. Which color(s) of light you tested seem to support photosynthesis?

d. Which color(s) of light you tested did not seem to support photosynthesis?

e. Starting from the sun, describe the process that allows you to see the color of your plant.

f. Why do certain colors support photosynthesis while others do not?

7A Protozoans

What are the characteristics of protozoans?

Most organisms in the Kingdom Protozoa consist of a single cell. How do these organisms move and gather food? In this investigation, you will examine amoeba, paramecium and euglena using the light microscope. You will observe their movement and characteristics. You will also develop a hypothesis about how each organisms gets food.

Materials
• Live euglena culture
• Live amoeba culture
• Live paramecium culture
• Depression slides
• Coverslips
• Corn syrup
• Light microscope
• Toothpicks
• Dropper

 Preparing slides of live protozoans

Observing amoeba

1. Place two drops of water into the chamber of the depression slide.
2. Slowly place a dropper into the amoeba culture. Be sure to place the dropper at the bottom of the culture since the amoeba will be located at the bottom of the jar.
3. Remove the dropper and place a single drop of the culture into the chamber of your compression slide.
4. Carefully, place a cover slip on top of the chamber and place under the microscope.
5. Using your medium power, bring the amoeba into view.
6. Once you have found the amoeba, switch to your high-power objective.
7. Make a sketch of what you observe under the microscope in Table 1.
8. Observe the movement of the amoeba and record your observations in Table 1.

Observing Paramecium and Euglena

1. Wash and thoroughly dry the chamber of the compression slide.
2. Repeat steps 1-3 above.
3. Place a drop of corn syrup into the chamber of the depression slide. Protozoa are very fast and corn syrup will slow the organisms so they may be viewed more easily under the microscope.
4. Place a single drop of paramecium culture into the chamber of the depression slide.
5. Using a toothpick carefully mix the corn syrup and the paramecium.
6. Carefully, place a cover slip on top of the chamber and place under the microscope.
7. Using your medium-power objective, bring the paramecium into view.
8. Once you have found the paramecium, switch to your high-power objective.
9. Sketch a picture of what you observe under the microscope in Table 1, paramecium.
10. Observe the movement of the paramecium and record your observations in Table 1.
11. Repeat the procedures this time using the euglena culture.

Table I: Protozoa observations

Amoeba	Paramecium	Euglena
Observations:	Observations	Observations:

2 ▶ Thinking about what you observed

a. Describe the way each organism (amoeba, paramecium, and euglena) moves. Which ones have structures for movement? Do those structures look like?

b. Do any of the organisms have a structure that resembles a mouth? Make a hypothesis about how each organism feeds.

c. Use the diagram (at left) to help you identify the structures of each organism. Label the structures you observed in your sketches.

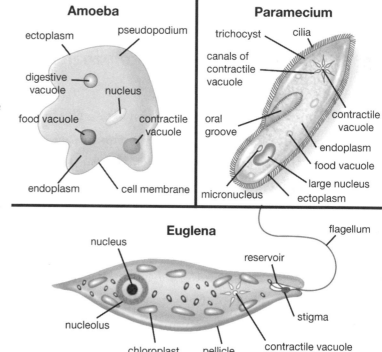

3 ▶ Exploring on your own

Protozoans are everywhere and will make their homes in a variety of water sources. Some protozoans cause sickness in humans. One species called *Giardia lamblia* is closely related to paramecium. It lives in freshwater sources. Research *Giardia* and write a short report. Use the key word "Giardia" in your Internet search. Include in your report the following information:

a. Where is *Giardia* found? How do people contract the disease?

b. What are the symptoms of the disease caused by Giardia?

c. How is the disease treated?

d. How can the disease caused by Giardia be prevented?

7B Investigating Pond Water

Which microscopic organisms are found in pond water?

If you took a single drop of water from a pond and looked at it under the microscope, you'd be lucky to find anything. To increase the number of organisms in your sample you can create a hay infusion. A hay infusion is a culture that uses water collected from a pond, stream, creek, or puddle and dried grass. You simply place dry grass a container of water and allow the culture to sit for approximately one week. At the end of the week, the culture will be teeming with different types of small microscopic organisms. In this investigation, you will make a hay infusion and then using what you have already learned, try to identify the micro-organisms.

Materials
• Glass jar
• Pond or creek water
• Hay or dry grass
• Milk
• Yeast
• Depression slides
• Coverslips
• Corn syrup
• Light microscope
• Dropper

 Setting up

Adding milk   Adding yeast

1. Place pond water into the glass jar until the jar is about half-filled.
2. Add several pieces of cut hay or dry grass to the jar.
3. Add a teaspoon of milk and a grain of yeast.
4. Loosely cover the jar with the lid. [Be sure not to tighten the lid of the jar completely since the organisms need oxygen.]
5. Place the jar in a warm place, in front of a window or in an incubator.
6. Check the hay infusion periodically, although it will take about a week for the organism growth to peak, spot checking the culture will ensure you see lots of different organisms.

Safety tip: The hay infusion will contain a large number of bacteria. Make sure you wash your hands completely after handling the hay infusion, samples, and depression slides.

Stop and think

a. What types of organisms do you think you will find under the microscope after a week?

b. Why is it important not to tighten the lid of the jar completely?

 **Doing the experiment**

1. Place a drop of water into your depression slide chamber.

2. Place a single drop of corn syrup into the well of the depression slide chamber. The corn syrup will slow the movement of the organisms without harming the organisms.

3. Remove jar's lid. Take a small drop of the water from the top of the jar and place it into the depression slide chamber.

4. Carefully, place a cover slip on top of the chamber and place under the microscope.

5. Using your low-power objective, bring the sample into focus. It is important to remember that the organisms will be moving quickly, so this step can be tricky.

6. Once you have found the correct plane of focus, switch to the high-power objective.

7. Make a sketch of what you observe under the microscope. It is possible you will see a number of organisms, and this is good. Make a careful sketch of every organism you see.

8. Once you have completed Steps 1-7, wash and thoroughly dry the chamber of the compression slide.

9. Repeat the procedures with drops of water taken from different areas of the jar.

10. Once you have completed your drawings, try to identify the organisms you have observed in your hay infusion. A sheet of photos will be provided by your teacher. Use other resources such as books or the Internet if needed.

Table I: Hay infusion observations

Sample Location: (top, middle, bottom)	Sketch of the Organism	Name of organism

4 ▸ Thinking about what you observed

a. How many different types of organisms did you identify?

b. What type of information did you use to help you identify the different organisms in your hay infusion?

c. Is there a difference between the types of organisms you observed at the bottom, middle, and top of the jar?

d. What sample contained the largest number of different organisms?

e. Which organisms belong to the Kingdom Protista? Which organisms do not?

8A Observing the Cell Cycle

How much time is spent in different stages of the cell cycle?

The life cycle of a cell is called the _cell cycle_. Interphase is the period a cell spends growing and performing its functions. _Mitosis_ is the part of the cell cycle where the chromosomes are divided into two new nuclei. Two daughter cells are formed, each containing a complete set of chromosomes. Mitosis has 4 phases: prophase, metaphase, anaphase, and telophase. After mitosis, the cytoplasm and its contents divide, separating the daughter cells (cytokinesis). In this investigation, you will determine the percentage of time a cell spends in interphase and the four stages of mitosis.

Materials

- Prepared whitefish blastula slides
- Prepared onion root tip slides
- Textbook
- Pencil for sketching
- Graph paper

 Setting up

1. Set up a microscope and turn on the light.
2. On the stage, place a slide containing a stained preparation of *Allium* (onion root tip).
3. Locate the growth zone of the onion root tip. It is just above the root cap at the very end.
4. Focus on low power, and then switch to medium or high power. Below are pictures of the four stages of mitosis. Use them to help you identify the different stages on the microscope slide.

Phases of mitosis (prepared slides of Allium)

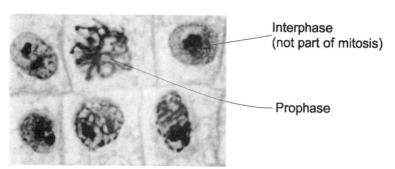

Interphase
(not part of mitosis)

Prophase

Interphase and Prophase (40X)

Metaphase (40X)

Anaphase (40X)

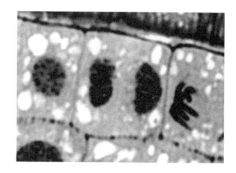

Telophase (40X)

2 ▶ Stop and think

a. How do the chromosomes look at each stage of the cell cycle (interphase, prophase, metaphase, anaphase, and telophase)?

b. Why is it important to recognize the differences in the appearance of the chromosomes at different stages?

3 ▶ Doing the experiment

1. Count the number of cells in interphase, prophase, metaphase, anaphase, and telophase. You'll have to move the slide around several times until you have covered the entire growth region. Record your data in Table 1 below.

2. Add up the total number of cells you counted and enter that value in Table 1.

3. Determine the percentage of time each cell will spend in each stage of the cell cycle. Use this formula:

(Number of cells in phase ÷ total number of cells) × 100

Record your values in Table 1.

Table 1: Number of cells and percentages

Stage of cell cycle	Number of cells in each stage	Time spent in each stage (%)
Interphase		
Prophase		
Metaphase		
Anaphase		
Telophase		

4 ▶ Thinking about what you observed

a. Make a line or bar graph of the data in Table 1. Place time spent on the *x*-axis and number of cells on they *y*-axis.

b. Of the four stages of mitosis, which one takes the most time to complete? Which is the shortest stage in duration?

c. Cytokinesis is a stage in the cell cycle that happens right after mitosis. In this stage, the cytoplasm is divided and the two daughter cells are separated. See if you can find an example of cytokinesis on your Allium slide.

d. Obtain a prepared slide of animal cells (whitefish blastula). Try to identify and sketch cells in different stages of the cell cycle. Make a sketch of a cell in interphase, prophase, metaphase, telophase, and anaphase. Try to identify and sketch cells in cytokinesis.

e. How is cytokinesis different in the animal cell?

8B Modeling Mitosis and Meiosis

How do sex cells end up with a haploid set of chromosomes?

You may have seen fruit flies buzzing around a bowl of fruit. They are tiny, but if you look closely you may see red or white eyes. Like all living organisms, fruit flies grow and reproduce. The diploid number of chromosomes in fruit flies is 8. In this investigation you will simulate mitosis and meiosis in fruit flies. Through the simulation you will identify how fruit fly sex cells end up with only 4 chromosomes; a haploid set.

Materials

- 16 pipe cleaners of 2 different colors and 4 matching lengths
- Poster board or large piece of paper
- Marker
- O-shaped cereal
- Colored pencils (red, green, blue, yellow)

 Setting up

1. Copy the chart (right) onto a piece of poster board. The circles represent a fruit fly body cell in different stages of the cell cycle and mitosis.

2. Your teacher will give you a set of pipe cleaners to represent chromosomes. One color will represent the mother and the other color will represent the father. Since chromosomes occur in homologous pairs, use the same length of pipe cleaner for each homologous pair. You should have two sets of four different lengths of pipe cleaners.

3. Begin by assembling a *diploid* set of chromosomes for a fruit fly as they exist during most of interphase (step 1 on the board). A diploid set contains pairs of homologous chromosomes. Each chromosome at this point will be a single strand. You will have an extra set of each length and color left over. Here is a diploid set:

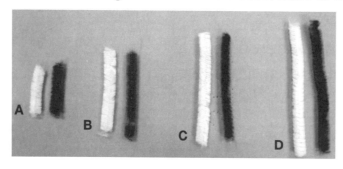

MITOSIS

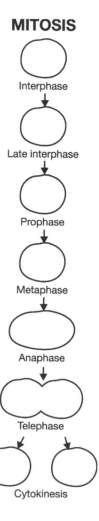

Interphase

Late interphase

Prophase

Metaphase

Anaphase

Telophase

Cytokinesis

Stop and think

a. What is the diploid number of chromosomes in a fruit fly?

b. How many homologous pairs of chromosomes does a fruit fly have?

c. In the diagram (right), name the steps that are part of mitosis.

d. Which steps are part of the rest of the cell cycle?

3 ▸ Modeling mitosis

1. In late interphase (step 2 on your board), the amount of DNA doubles. That means each chromosome now doubles. Select a matching pipe cleaner (same length and color) for each chromosome and slide both through a piece of cereal. You now should have a set of eight doubled chromosomes arranged in homologous pairs.

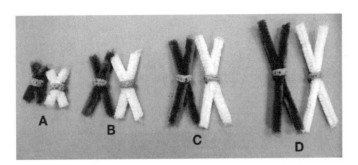

2. Review the mitosis diagram in Chapter 8 of your textbook and move the chromosomes through the rest of the steps on your board.

4 ▸ Applying your knowledge

a. Fill in Table 1 with the correct information.

Table 1: Cell cycle and mitosis in fruit flies

Step	Number of cells	Number of chromosomes in each nucleus	Number of homologous pairs in each nucleus
Interphase			
Cytokinesis			

b. What is the purpose of mitosis?

c. A diploid set of human chromosomes contains 23 homologous pairs (46 chromosomes). Fill in Table 2 with the correction information regarding human body cells.

Table 2: Cell cycle and mitosis in humans

Step	Number of cells	Number of chromosomes in each nucleus	Number of homologous pairs in each nucleus
Interphase			
Cytokinesis			

d. Why is it necessary to double the amount of genetic material before mitosis begins?

e. The two daughter cells end up with an exact copy of the genetic material from the parent cell. How does your simulation support this statement?

Meiosis is the process of producing sex cells with a haploid set of chromosomes. _Haploid_ means half the number of chromosomes as the original cell. A haploid cell contains one chromosome from each homologous pair.

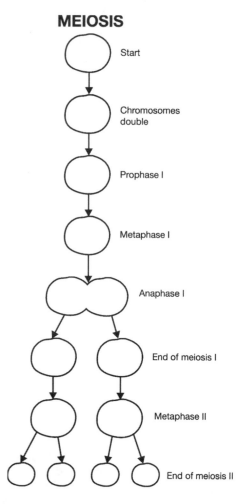

1. Turn over your poster board and copy the diagram (right) onto the other side. Fill the entire space on the board with your drawing.

2. Begin by assembling a diploid set of chromosomes for the fruit fly as you did in part 1. Place the chromosomes, in homologous pairs, in the first nucleus on your poster.

3. Like mitosis, before meiosis begins, the chromosomes double. Add a similar pipe cleaner to each chromosome and attach with a piece of cereal as you did in part 1.

4. Unlike mitosis which has only one cell division, meiosis has two divisions (meiosis I and meiosis II). Using the meiosis diagram in Chapter 8 of your textbook as a guide, move your chromosomes through meiosis I and meiosis II.

5. Fill in Table 3 below as you move your chromosomes through the chart.

Table 3: Meiosis

Step	Number of cells	Number of chromosomes in each cell	Number of homologous pairs in each cell	Diploid or haploid number?
Start of meiosis				
End of meiosis I				
End of meiosis II				

 Thinking about what you observed

a. What happens to the homologous pairs of chromosomes in meiosis I?

b. At the end of meiosis I, how does the number of chromosomes in each new cell compare to the original number of chromosomes in the parent cell? (Is it diploid or haploid?)

c. At the end of meiosis II, how does the number of chromosomes in each new cell compare to the original number of chromosomes in the parent cell?

Exploring on your own

If time permits, you can model what happens during fertilization.

1. Sketch the chart (right) onto a blank piece of paper.
2. Remove the chromosomes from a sex cell you created during the investigation and combine this with the chromosomes of a sex cell from a different group. This is less complicated if you combine with a group that has different color pipe cleaners from yours.

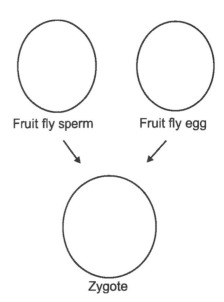

a. What is the end result of fertilization in terms of chromosome number?

b. Do the cells of the new organism have a diploid or haploid set of chromosomes?

c. What would happen if the sperm cell and egg cell did not reduce the number of chromosomes before fertilization? Model this with two diploid sets of chromosomes.

d. You have 23 pairs of chromosomes in your body cells. Why do your chromosomes occur in pairs? For each pair, where does each chromosome come from?

9A Observing Human Traits

How much do traits vary in your classroom?

Traits are physical characteristics you inherit from your parents. In this investigation, you will take an inventory of your observable traits and compare these to the observable traits of your classmates. You will then take inventory of students and teachers in your school. Finally, you will determine the frequency of each trait in your school's population.

Materials

- PTC paper
- Pencils
- Calculator

 Observing your own traits

The graphic below shows seven different human traits. Each trait has two different forms. Study the chart below, then follow the procedures carefully.

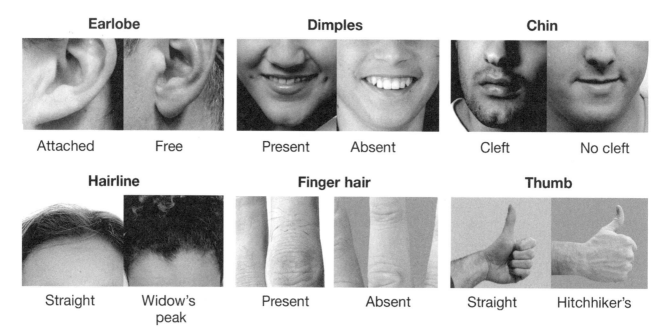

Earlobe		Dimples		Chin	
Attached	Free	Present	Absent	Cleft	No cleft

Hairline		Finger hair		Thumb	
Straight	Widow's peak	Present	Absent	Straight	Hitchhiker's

1. Working with a partner, observe which form you have for trait A through F. Circle your form of each trait in Table 1.
   NOTE: For finger hair, even if you have only one hair on any of your mid-digits, you have finger hair.
2. Wash and dry your hands. For trait G, your teacher will give you and your partner a piece of PTC paper. Taste the paper and circle your form of the trait in Table 1.

Safety tip: Never taste any substance in the laboratory unless directed by your teacher.

Table 1: Inventory of traits

Trait	Form 1	Form 2
A. Earlobe	Free	Attached
B. Dimples	Absent	Present
C. Chin	Cleft	No cleft
D. Hairline	Widow's peak	Straight
E. Finger hair	Present	Absent
F. Thumb	Straight thumb	Hitchhiker's thumb
G. PTC tasting	Can taste	Cannot taste

2 ▶ Stop and think

a. For earlobes only, how many students in your class do you think will share the same form (free or attached) as you? Explain your reasoning.

b. Do you think any of your classmates will have the same form of *all* traits as you? Make a prediction about how many of your classmates will have the same form of all seven traits as you.

3 ▶ Collecting class data

1. Enter your results in the chart your teacher has placed on the chalkboard or overhead projector.

2. Record the numbers from the chart into columns 2 and 4 of Table 2 below.

Table 2: Class data for observable traits

Trait	Number of students with Form 1	Frequency of students with Form 1	Number of students with Form 2	Frequency of students with Form 2
A. Earlobe				
B. Dimples				
C. Chin				
D. Hairline				
E. Finger hair				
F. Thumb				
G. PTC tasting				

3. Calculate the frequency of each form of the trait for your class. Use this formula:

(No. of students with form of trait ÷ Total number of students in class) × 100

4. Make a bar graph of the data in Table 2. Your graph should compare frequencies for each form of each trait. Put traits on the *x*-axis and frequency on the *y*-axis.

49

4 ▲ Thinking about what you observed

a. For each trait, which form was most common, Form 1 or Form 2?

b. Why do you think one form is more common than the other?

c. Do you think your classroom population is typical of a larger population such as your entire school or community? Explain your answer.

d. Traits are controlled by factors called _genes_. For each trait listed in Table 1, you get one gene from your mother and one gene from your father. For each trait, there is a dominant form and a recessive form. The _dominant_ gene masks the effect of the _recessive_ gene for the trait. Based on your class data, which form of each trait do you think is the dominant form? Explain your answer.

e. The dominant and recessive forms for each trait you studied are listed below. Was the recessive form of any trait more frequent than the dominant form? Make a hypothesis that explains this result.

Trait	Dominant form	Recessive form
A. Earlobe	Free	Attached
B. Dimples	No dimples	Dimples present
C. Chin	Cleft present	No cleft
D. Hairline	Widow's peak	Straight
E. Finger hair	Finger hair present	No finger hair
F. Thumb	Straight thumb	Hitchhiker's thumb
G. PTC tasting	Taster	Non-taster

5 ▲ Exploring on your own

a. Pick any trait (except for PTC tasting) and gather data about the trait from a larger population. Examples of a larger population include your school, neighborhood, and place of worship. Follow these steps:
1. Make a hypothesis about what you will observe.
2. Collect data from as many people as you can and record your results in a data table.
3. Graph your data.
4. Present your results to the class for discussion.

b. Do you think people who are related to each other would show more similarity among the seven traits than unrelated people? Design an experiment to test your hypothesis.

9B Crazy Traits

What role does chance play in an organism's heredity?

Your traits are determined by the genes you inherit from your parents. For each gene, you get at least one allele from your mother and one allele from your father. The alleles you end up with are determined by two factors: (1) the genotypes of your parents; and (2) the allele from each parent you inherit. The alleles you inherit from each parent are determined by chance. In this investigation, you will play a game that will help you learn about inheritance.

Materials

- Crazy Traits game
- Name tags
- Markers

Determining the genotype

1. The first trait you will flip for is gender. Choose the male sex chromosome coin (**X** on one side and **Y** on the other) and the female sex chromosome coin (**X** on both sides). Place both coins in the plastic cup and shake. Toss the coins onto the table and record your results in Table 1.

2. Next, flip coins to determine the allele for each of the other traits your creature inherits from each parent. In this activity, we will assume that both parents have the same genotype for all traits (*Tt*). You will need a blue (egg) coin with a capital *T* on one side and a lower case *t* on the other side. You will also a green (sperm) coin with a capital *T* on one side and a lower case *t* on the other side.

3. Flip the coins for the next trait—skin color. Place the coins in the plastic cup. Shake the cup and toss the two coins onto the lab table. The side that lands up on each coin represents the sperm and egg that unite during fertilization. Record the allele from each parent and genotype in columns 2, 3, and 4 of the first row of Table 1.

4. Repeat this procedure for traits 2 through 14.

2 Stop and Think

a. What information do the letters on the sperm and egg coins indicate: alleles, genotype, or phenotype?

b. For the sperm coin, what are the chances of getting a *T* or getting a *t*? State your answer as a fraction and a percent.

c. For the egg coin, what are the chances of getting a *T* or getting a *t*? State your answer as a fraction or a percent.

d. When both coins are flipped at once, what are your chances of getting each of the following combinations: *TT*, *Tt*, or *tt*? Make a punnett square to show the cross. State your answer for each as a fraction and a percent.

Table 1: Genotypes and phenotypes of offspring for Part 1

Trait	Allele from mother	Allele from father	Genotype	Phenotype
1. Gender				
2. Skin color				
3. Leg				
4. Foot				
5. Arms				
6. Hands				
7. Eye color				
8. Eyebrows				
9. Beak				
10. Ears				
11. Antenna				
12. Antenna shape				
13. Tail				
14. Wings				

3 ▶ Building your creature

1. Once you have completed columns 2 through 4 of Table 1, use Table 2 (next page) to look up the phenotype for each trait. Record the phenotype for each trait in column 5 of Table 1.

2. Once you have completed Table 1, select the correct body parts to build your creature.

3. Carefully assemble your creature.

4. Give your creature a name and make it a name tag. Write the gender of your creature on the name tag.

5. Place your creature on the table at the front of your classroom.

4 ▶ Thinking about what you observed

a. Examine the creatures. Do any of them look exactly alike? Why or why not?

b. How does this investigation explain why siblings may resemble each other, but never look exactly alike (unless they are identical twins)?

c. Count the number of males and number of females. Does the number of each match the chances of getting a male or female in the game? Why or why not?

d. Which trait(s) are examples of complete dominance?

e. Which trait(s) are examples of incomplete dominance?

f. Which trait(s) are examples of codominance?

Table 2: Key to genotypes and phenotypes

Trait	Genotypes and phenotypes
1. Gender	*XX* - female *XY* - male
2. Skin color	*TT* - red *Tt* - purple *tt* - blue
3. Leg	*TT* - short *Tt* - short *tt* - long
4. Foot	*TT* - webbed *Tt* - webbed *tt* - talons
5. Arms	*TT* - long *Tt* - long *tt* - short
6. Hands	*TT* - paws *Tt* - paws *tt* - claws
7. Eye color	*TT* - red *Tt* - one red and one green *tt* - green
8. Eyebrows	*TT* - unibrow *Tt* - unibrow *tt* - separate
9. Beak	*TT* - trumpet *Tt* - trumpet *tt* - crusher
10. Ears	*TT* - elephant *Tt* - elephant *tt* - mouse
11. Antenna	*TT* - long *Tt* - long *tt* - short
12. Antenna shape	*TT* - knob *Tt* - knob *tt* - star
13. Tail	*TT* - long *Tt* - short *tt* - none
14. Wings	*TT* - no wings *Tt* - no wings *tt* - wings

 Exploring on your own

If time permits, work with another group whose creature is the opposite gender. Follow the steps below to create offspring of the couple:

1. Record the genotypes of each parent in the first column of Table 3 on the next page.

2. First, toss for gender using the male and female sex chromosome coins.

3. For each trait, you'll need to use the correct egg and sperm coins for each parent. Use the data in Table 1 to find the parents' genotype for each trait. Then, select the egg and sperm coin that has the same alleles as the genotype. For example, if the father's genotype for skin color is *TT*, choose the sperm coin that has a capital *T* on both sides of the coin. If the mother's genotype for skin color is *tt*, place the egg coin that has a lower case *t* on both sides of the coin.

4. Place both coins in the plastic cup, shake, and toss out onto the table. Record your results in the fourth column of Table 3.

5. Use Table 2 to look up the phenotypes. Record the phenotypes of the offspring in the last column of Table 3.

Table 3: Offspring genotypes and phenotypes for Part 5

Trait	Genotype of mother for the trait	Genotype of father for the trait	Genotype of offspring (after flipping)	Phenotype of offspring
1. Gender				
2. Skin color				
3. Leg				
4. Foot				
5. Arms				
6. Hands				
7. Eye color				
8. Eyebrows				
9. Beak				
10. Ears				
11. Antenna				
12. Antenna shape				
13. Tail				
14. Wings				

6 ► Applying what you learned

a. Which parent does your offspring share the most traits with, the mother, father, or both equally?

b. Why do you need to choose different egg and sperm coins for each trait and for each parent?

c. What is the process that flipping the sex cell coins represents? Why is this process important?

d. There is always a 50% chance of having a male offspring. Explain why this statement is true. You may use a diagram to help explain.

e. In part 1, you started off with both parents having identical genotypes for all traits. Use what you have learned in the investigation to explain why this is unrealistic in nature.

f. CHALLENGE! Make punnett squares to show possible genotypes and phenotypes for each trait you flipped for in Part 5. For each, list the chances for each phenotype as a ratio and as a percent.

10A The DNA Molecule

What is the structure of the DNA molecule?

Deoxyribonucleic acid (DNA) is the hereditary molecule. DNA is made of individual units called nucleotides. Each nucleotide is made of a phosphate group, a sugar (deoxyribose), and a nitrogen base. The DNA molecule looks like a twisted ladder. The phosphate and sugar form the sides of the molecule. Each rung contains a pair of *bases* held together by hydrogen bonds. There are four bases: thymine (**T**), adenine (**A**), guanine (**G**), and cytosine (**C**). **T** and **A** always pair up and **G** and **C** always pair up. In this investigation you will model the structure of DNA using beads to represent the different parts of the DNA molecule.

Materials

- Red pop beads
- White pop beads
- Yellow pop beads
- Green pop beads
- Orange pop beads
- Blue pop beads
- Clear plastic connectors

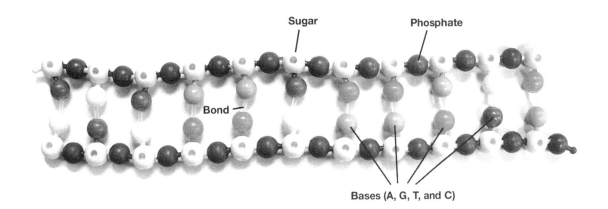

Sugar Phosphate Bond Bases (A, G, T, and C)

1 ▲ Setting Up

1. Gather the required materials. Use Table 1 as a key for creating your DNA model.

Table 1: DNA model components

Pop bead color	Molecule
Red	Phosphate group
White	Sugar (deoxyribose)
	Bases:
Blue	Cytosine (**C**)
Orange	Guanine (**G**)
Yellow	Adenine (**A**)
Green	Thymine (**T**)

2 ▶ Doing the Experiment

1. Begin by creating two phosphate-sugar "backbones" that will provide the framework on which to build each strand of your DNA molecule. Connect alternating white and red pop beads. Each backbone should contain 10 red pop beads and 10 white pop beads.

2. Repeat step 1 to create the second phosphate-sugar backbone.

3. Attach a **base** to each sugar on <u>one</u> of the phosphate-sugar backbones. We will call this the **original DNA strand**. At this point, the order of the bases does not matter. Use blue to represent **C**, orange to represent **G**, yellow to represent **A** and green to represent **T** (see Table 1).

4. Once you have created the original DNA strand, complete the first two columns of Table 2. Place the color of the bead followed by the letter of the base in order as they appear in your model.

Table 2: DNA molecule data

Original strand		Complimentary strand	
pop bead color	base	complimentary base	pop bead color

5. Once you have indicated the sequence of bases on the original DNA strand in Table 2, determine the base sequence for the **complimentary DNA strand**. Remember, **T** always pairs with **A** and **G** always pairs with **C**.

6. In Table 2, indicate the name of the complementary base and the color of the corresponding pop bead.

7. Using the second phosphate-sugar backbone that you created in step 2, make the complementary DNA strand using the information contained in Table 2.

8. Once you have created the complimentary DNA strand, use the clear plastic connectors to "bond" the base pairs together. These connectors represent the weak bonds that keep the base pairs together.

9. Draw a sketch of your DNA molecule in Table 3.

10. Hold the model from the top, and gently twist the DNA ladder to the right. You should see that the DNA looks like a spiral staircase. The model now represents the helical structure of DNA. Your teacher may instruct you to take your model and attach all the DNA models together to make a longer strand of DNA. Do not do this until instructed by your teacher.

Table 3: DNA molecule sketch

3 ▲ Thinking about what you observed

a. Which molecules make up the backbone of the DNA molecule?

b. Why is DNA called "deoxyribose nucleic acid"?

c. What type of bond keeps the bases paired together?

d. Which base always pairs with adenine? Which base always pairs with cytosine?

4 ▲ Exploring on your own

Watson and Crick were awarded the Nobel Prize for their work in determining the structure of DNA. However, the work of many scientists led to the final determination of the structure of DNA. One such scientist was Rosalind Franklin. Do some research (library or internet) to learn more about Rosalind Franklin. Try and figure out what she was studying and why this helped Watson and Crick determine the structure of DNA. Think about why her research might have gone unnoticed for so long.

10B DNA Forensics

How can DNA be used to solve a "crime?"

You have learned that DNA is the molecule that carries the hereditary information. Each individual is genetically unique, except in cases of identical twins, and as a result your DNA becomes a molecular fingerprint. This molecular fingerprint can be used to identify an individual with a great degree of certainty and is used in the field of forensic science. Scientists use DNA left at crime scenes to identify a person who may have been involved in a crime. In this Investigation, you will use DNA to solve a fictional crime.

Materials

- Red pop beads
- White pop beads
- Yellow pop beads
- Green pop beads
- Orange pop beads
- Blue pop beads
- Clear plastic connectors
- DNA sequences
- Envelope containing the identity of the DNA sequence

 Doing the Experiment

Today, someone left your teacher an apple with a note, "You are a super teacher!" But between the time the apple was left and the time your teacher returned to class, a bite has been taken out of it! Imagine that DNA has been collected from the "crime scene." A DNA sample has also been collected from suspects. Your lab group will help solve the case by building a portion of a DNA molecule from one of the suspects. Then, you will compare your DNA model with others in the class. Can you solve the mystery?

1. Gather the required materials. Use Table 1 as a key for creating your DNA molecule.

Table 1: DNA model components

Pop bead color	Molecule
Red	Phosphate group
White	Sugar (deoxyribose)
Blue	Cytosine
Orange	Guanine
Yellow	Adenine
Green	Thymine

2. Your teacher will give each group an envelope. The DNA sample number is printed on the outside. The sequence of bases on one strand is also provided.

Table 2: DNA sample data

DNA sample number:	
Number of bases:	
Number of sugar molecules:	
Number of phosphate molecules:	

3. Begin by creating the phosphate and sugar backbone of the DNA molecule. Determine the number of bases and indicate this number in Table 2.

4. Recall that the bases attach to the sugar molecules. Calculate the number of sugar molecules that will be needed and record this in Table 2. Since the backbone is

alternating phosphate and sugar molecules, calculate the number of phosphate molecules that will be needed. Record this in Table 2.

5. Using your calculations recorded in Table 2, create two phosphate-sugar backbones that provide the framework to build your DNA model.

6. Using the base sequence provided by your teacher, create your DNA model. Table 1 contains the base color coding for the pop beads that will be used in creating your sample of DNA.

7. Once you have created your DNA sample, wait for instructions from your teacher.

8. Once everyone in the class is done creating their DNA models, compare your DNA model with those of your classmates. Once a match is found, each group should open their envelopes to determine the source of the DNA sample.

2 ◣ Thinking about what you observed

a. Who was the person that took a bite from the apple on your teacher's desk?

b. Why is it important to correctly construct the DNA model of the different samples?

c. How could mistakes in the construction of the original models lead to a mistake in the identity of the suspect?

3 ◣ Exploring on your own

A technique called DNA fingerprinting produces an image of patterns made by a person's DNA. Using an enzyme, scientists "cut" DNA strands in specific places. The DNA fragments are injected into a gel and an electric current is applied. As the fragments migrate across the gel, they create patterns. Those patterns (DNA fingerprints) are related to the base sequences along the DNA strand. Suppose a serious crime has been committed. There are six suspects. Since blood was found at the crime scene, DNA fingerprints can be produced. Blood is drawn from the six suspects and DNA fingerprints are produced. By comparing the DNA fingerprints of the suspects to the blood from the crime scene, police quickly determine who committed the crime. Can you tell who committed the crime?

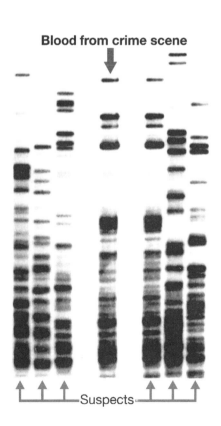

Blood from crime scene

Suspects

11A Crazy Adaptations

How does the environment influence traits?

When Darwin examined the finches he saw on the Galapagos Islands, he noticed differences in the appearance of different species. He noticed that the shape of finch beaks varied according to their primary food source. In this investigation, you will build a creature that is adapted to its environment and describe its adaptations. Then you will play the game of Adaptation Survivor.

Materials
- Crazy Traits game
- Dice

 Determining your environment

Roll the dice for each environmental variable and record your results in Table 1.

Table 1: Environmental data

Environmental variable	Possibilities with roll of the dice	Outcome
Surface color	1, 2 = Blue soil 3,4 = Purple soil 5,6 = Red soil	
Food source	1, 2 = chocolate candies 3, 4 = jumbo marshmallows 5, 6 = milk shake	
Predator	1,2 = *Hawkus giganticus* (flies over the land and snatches prey by their antennae) 3,4 = *Frightus catus* (afraid of water but can run very fast) 5,6 = *Microtus pesticus* (a blind army ant that crawls on the ground and attacks in large groups but cannot fly)	
Topography	1,2 = flat 3,4 = mountainous 5,6 = swampy	

Stop and think

a. What is an adaptation? Where do adaptations come from?

b. What kinds of adaptations would your creature need in order to survive in the environment in Table 1?

3 ▶ Choosing your traits

1. Think about adaptations that would help an organism survive in the environment you determined in Part 1. Choose the traits from Table 2 below that would be adaptations for the environment.

Table 2: Possible genotypes and phenotypes of traits

Trait	Genotypes and phenotypes
1. Skin color	*TT* - red *Tt* - purple *tt* - blue
2. Eye color	*TT* - red *Tt* - one red and one green *tt* - green
3. Eyebrows	*TT* - unibrow *Tt* - unibrow *tt* - separate
4. Beak	*TT* - trumpet *Tt* - trumpet *tt* - crusher
5. Ears	*TT* - elephant *Tt* - elephant *tt* - mouse
6. Leg	*TT* - short *Tt* - short *tt* - long
7. Foot	*TT* - webbed *Tt* - webbed *tt* - talons
8. Arms	*TT* - long *Tt* - long *tt* - short
9. Hands	*TT* - paws *Tt* - paws *tt* - claws
10. Antenna	*TT* - long *Tt* - long *tt* - short
11. Antenna shape	*TT* - knob *Tt* - knob *tt* - star
12. Tail	*TT* - long *Tt* - short *tt* - none
13. Wings	*TT* - no wings *Tt* - no wings *tt* - wings

2. Complete Table 3 by filling in the genotype and phenotype for each trait you choose.

3. Tell whether each trait is an adaptation or not. If a trait is an adaptation, explain how it will help your creature survive in their environment. Record your answers in the last column of Table 3.

Table 3: Genotype and phenotype of your creature

Trait	Genotype	Phenotype	Adaptation? If yes, explain
1. Skin color			
2. Eye color			
3. Eyebrows			
4. Beak			
5. Ears			
6. Leg			
7. Foot			
8. Arms			
9. Hands			
10. Antenna			
11. Antenna shape			
12. Tail			
13. Wings			

Analyzing the data

a. Build your creature.

b. Describe the adaptations your creature has for surviving in its environment. Be creative!

c. Compare your environment and creature to the environment and creatures of the other groups in your class.

 Playing the Game of Adaptation Survivor

Refer to Table 3 for the phenotypes of your creature. You will now see if your creature can survive the unpredictable conditions of a changing world. The object of the game is to be the last surviving creature in your environment. You earn or lose points based upon whether your creature's particular set of traits are adaptations for survival. **When your creature earns a minus-three total, it becomes extinct.**

1. Your teacher will choose someone to draw the first Environment Card and read it aloud. Each card describes two environmental conditions or events - read only the *one* condition that is facing you as you draw it. For each environmental condition, your creature can:

    a. thrive (+1);

    b. be pushed closer to extinction (-1);

    c. or, have no effect (+0).

    The scoring is based upon your creature's phenotype for a given trait. For example, if a very successful land predator finds its way onto your island, your only chance for survival may be the set of wings that your creature possesses. This would give you an advantage over a non-winged creature. For that Environment Card you will earn a plus one (+1). If your creature does not possess wings then you earn a minus one (-1).

2. There are some special cards in the deck, called Catastrophe Cards. If one of these cards is drawn, you might earn a minus one, regardless of your characteristic makeup.

3. Your class will continue drawing Environment Cards. Your teacher will keep track of points on the chalkboard. (For our example, your teacher may write "Wings +1/No Wings -1."

4. Play until there is only one surviving creature. This is the winner of the game. NOTE: If a final card wipes out the last two or more creatures (complete extinction), then there is no winning survivor. Do you think that a complete extinction like this is likely to happen often? Why or why not?

11B Natural Selection

How does evolution work?

In the last investigation, you learned that there are favorable and unfavorable adaptations in a population. Favorable adaptations help an individual survive and are passed on to the next generation. In this investigation you will simulate the process of natural selection. As you proceed, think about how a new species forms.

Materials

- 100 red jelly beans
- 100 yellow jelly beans
- 100 green jelly beans
- large sheet of red paper
- large sheet of yellow paper
- large sheet of green paper
- 3 Petri dishes

 Thinking about what you will do

Imagine a population of tiny, candy creatures called *yum-yums* that live on Ketchup Island. Their main predator is a large, hungry creature called a *gobbler*. Gobblers can only open their eyes for one second at a time out of every 10 seconds. Yum-yums are the gobblers favorite food because they taste so sweet.

Yum-yums normally have a red shell. But a mutation in the gene for shell color causes green- or yellow-shelled individuals. The percent of each shell color in the population is shown in Table 1.

Table 1: Yum-yum population on Ketchup Island

Shell color	Percent of population	Number of individuals
Red (R)	80	120
Yellow (Y)	10	15
Green (G)	10	15
Total population on Ketchup Island		150

1. In the simulation, you will use a large sheet of red paper to represent Ketchup Island. You will use colored jelly beans (red, yellow, and green) to represent yum-yums. You will play the role of the gobbler.

2. Set up your yum-yum population on a sheet of red paper with the correct number of each color of jelly bean from Table 1. Scatter the jelly beans over the paper in random order. DO NOT EAT ANY JELLY BEANS UNTIL YOU HAVE COMPLETED THE INVESTIGATION!

 Stop and think

a. Is there genetic variation in the yum-yum population? Explain your answer.

b. Why is genetic variation important in a population?

c. Explain why most of the yum-yum population is red. Use the following terms in your explanation: *adaptation*, *allele*, *phenotype*, *natural selection*, and *evolution*.

3 ▶ Setting up the experiment

A huge storm has struck! The storm has blown 1/3 of the yum-yum population onto Mustard Island. It has blown another 1/3 of the population onto Relish Island. The remaining 1/3 of the population remains on Ketchup Island.

1. Remove 40 red, 5 yellow, and 5 green jelly beans from Ketchup Island. Scatter them randomly onto a sheet of yellow paper (Mustard Island).

2. Remove another 40 red, 5 yellow, and 5 green jelly beans from Ketchup Island and scatter them randomly over a sheet of green paper (Relish Island).

3. You should now have 40 red, 5 yellow, and 5 green jelly beans remaining on Ketchup Island.

4. Complete the first row in Table 2. First, enter the number of individuals of each color on each Island. Then, calculate the percent of each shell color and enter in Table 2. Ketchup Island is done for you. To calculate percent, use the formula below:

$$\% \text{ of color} = \frac{\text{number of the color}}{\text{total number of jelly beans}} \times 100$$

Table 2: Yum-yum generations

Generations	Ketchup Is.		Mustard Is.		Relish Is.	
	Number of individuals	Percent of population	Number of individuals	Percent of population	Number of individuals	Percent of population
Parent	R = 40 Y = 5 G = 5	80 10 10	R Y G		R Y G	
1	R Y G		R Y G		R Y G	
2	R Y G		R Y G		R Y G	
3	R Y G		R Y G		R Y G	
4	R Y G		R Y G		R Y G	
5	R Y G		R Y G		R Y G	

4 ▸ Making a hypothesis

a. There are three steps to species formation: *isolation*, *adaptation*, and *differentiation*. Which step does Part 3 simulate?

b. What do you think will happen to shell colors in each population of yum-yums over time? Write your prediction as a hypothesis.

5 ▸ Doing the experiment

1. You will need six students in your group. You will need two students for each island. For each island, one student is the *timer* and the other is the *gobbler*.
2. The gobbler sits in front of the island and closes her/his eyes.
3. The timer waits 10 seconds and then says: OPEN! The gobbler opens his eyes for one second, grabs the first jelly bean he sees, places it in a Petri dish, then closes his eyes again. This process is repeated 10 times.
4. Count the number of jelly beans left of each color and enter in the next row of Table 2. Add up the total number of jelly beans and calculate the percent of each color and enter into Table 2.
5. Add 5 jelly beans of each color to your island. This step represents reproduction.
6. Repeat steps 2 through 5 for a total of 5 generations.
7. Enter the data for the other two islands from the other members of your group.

6 ▸ Analyzing the data

a. Make a *bar graph* of your data for each island. Plot generations (parent through 5) on the *x*-axis and percent of each color on the *y*-axis. Be sure to put a title on your graph and label the axes.

b. Compare the percentages of each shell color on each island for each generation. What changes, if any, occurred on each island over time? Does your data support your hypothesis from Part 4?

c. How does this investigation simulate natural selection?

d. Explain how populations on each island may become different species over time.

7 ▸ Exploring on your own

a. Yum-yums have a sweet taste that is preferred by gobblers. Suppose a mutation occurred in the gene for taste. The mutation resulted in offspring with a bitter taste. What would you expect to happen to that mutation over time? Explain what would happen to the percent of yum-yums with the mutation after many generations.

b. Make a list of other mutations in yum-yums that could result in organisms that are better adapted for survival. Be creative!

12A Relative Dating

How can you determine the sequence of past events?

Earth is very old and many of its features were formed before people came along to study them. For that reason, studying Earth now is like detective work—using clues to uncover fascinating stories. The work of geologists and paleontologists is very much like the work of forensic scientists at a crime scene. In all three fields, the ability to put events in their proper order is the key to unraveling the hidden story.

Materials

- Construction paper
- Colored markers
- Tape
- Glue
- Scissors
- Different colors of modeling clay
- Different colors of sand or soil
- Rocks
- An empty shoe box or a clear tank for clues

 Sequencing events after a thunderstorm

Carefully examine this illustration. It contains evidence of following events:

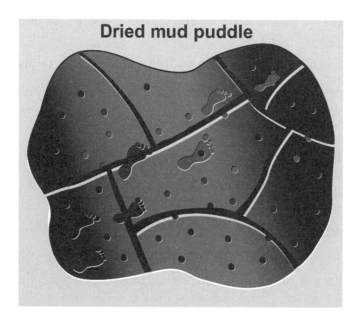

Dried mud puddle

- The baking heat of the sun caused cracks to formed in the dried mud puddle.
- A thunderstorm began.
- The mud puddle dried.
- A child ran through the mud puddle.
- Hailstones fell during the thunderstorm.

a. From the clues in the illustration, sequence the events listed above in the order in which they happened.

b. Write a brief story that explains the appearance of the dried mud puddle and includes all the events. In your story, justify the order of the events.

2 ▶ Determining the relative ages of rock formations

Relative dating is an Earth science term that describes the set of principles and techniques used to sequence geologic events and determine the relative age of rock formations. Below are graphics that illustrate some of these basic principles used by geologists. You will find that these concepts are easy to understand.

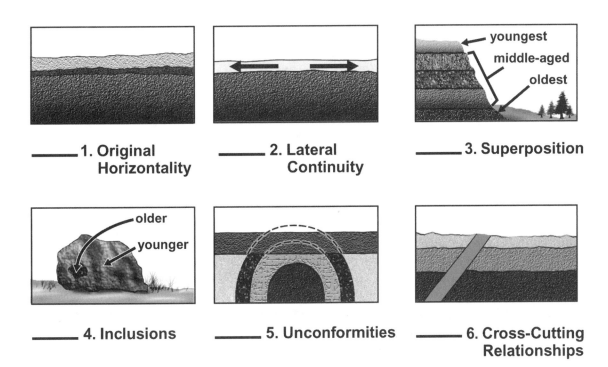

_____ 1. Original Horizontality

_____ 2. Lateral Continuity

_____ 3. Superposition

_____ 4. Inclusions

_____ 5. Unconformities

_____ 6. Cross-Cutting Relationships

Match each principle to its explanation. Write the letter of the explanation in the space provided under each graphic.

Explanations:

a.   In undisturbed rock layers, the oldest layer is at the bottom and the youngest layer is at the top.

b.   In some rock formations, layers or parts of layers may be missing. This is often due to **erosion**. Erosion by water or wind removes sediment from exposed surfaces. Erosion often leaves a new flat surface with some of the original material missing.

c.   Sediments are originally deposited in horizontal layers.

d.   Any feature that cuts across rock layers is younger than the layers.

e.   Sedimentary layers or lava flows extend sideways in all directions until they thin out or reach a barrier.

f.   Any part of a previous rock layer, like a piece of stone, is older than the layer containing it.

3 ▲ Sequencing events in a geologic cross-section

Understanding how a land formation was created with its many layers of soil begins with the same time-ordering process you used in Part 1. Geologists use logical thinking and geology principles like the ones described in Part 2 to determine the order of events for a geologic formation. Cross-sections of Earth, like the one shown below, are our best records of what has happened in the past.

Rock bodies in this cross-section are labeled A through H. One of these rock bodies is an **intrusion**. Intrusions occur when molten rock called *magma* penetrates into layers from below. The magma is always younger than the layers that it penetrates. Likewise, a fault is always younger than the layers that have faulted. A *fault* is a crack or break occurs across rock layers, and the term *faulting* is used to describe the occurrence of a fault. The broken layers may move so that one side of the fault is higher than the other. Faulted layers may also tilt.

a. Put the rock bodies illustrated below in order based on when they formed.

b. Relative to the other rock bodies, when did the fault occur?

c. Compared with the formation of the rock bodies, when did the stream form? Justify your answer.

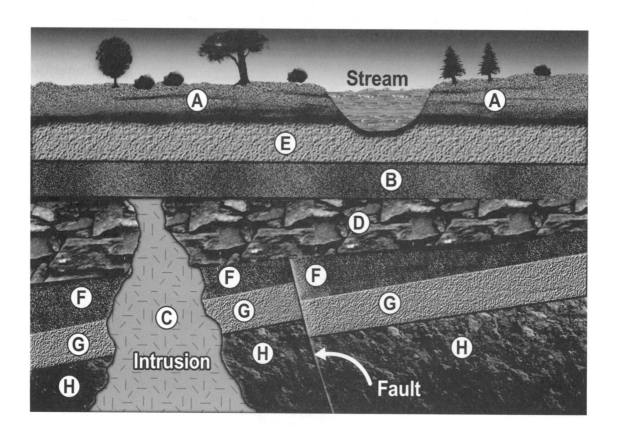

Creating clues for a story

Now, your teacher will provide your group with some materials. Using these materials, create a set of clues that will tell a story. Then, give another group in your class the opportunity to sequence the clues into a story. Follow these guidelines in setting up your story:

- Set up a situation that includes clues that represent at least five events.

- Each of the five events must happen independently. In other words, two events cannot have happened at the same time.

- Use at least one geology principle that you learned in this Investigation.

- Answer the questions below.

a. Describe your set of clues in a paragraph. Include enough details in your paragraph so that someone can re-create the set of clues.

b. What relative dating principles are represented with your set of clues? Explain how these principles are represented.

c. Now, have a group of your classmates put your set of clues in order. When they are done, evaluate their work. Write a short paragraph that explains how they did and whether or not they figured out the correct sequence of clues. Describe the clue they missed if they made an error.

5 **Exploring further**

a. In the Investigation, you organized your thoughts into stories. How does organizing your thoughts as stories help you understand science?

b. Cross-sections like the illustration in Part 3 have been used to help explain amazing events like the collision of continents or an ancient earthquake. If two continents collided, what features might you see in a cross-section of land?

c. Read about forensic science on the Internet or in your local library. How is forensic science like life science? Write a short paragraph that compares and contrasts these two branches of science.

12B Fossils in Time

How are fossils useful evidence for continental drift?

<u>Fossils</u> are the remains or evidence of living organism. Fossils come in different forms, including casts, molds, imprints, amber, and ice. Scientists can learn a great deal about life and the history of Earth using fossils. Fossils are useful evidence for understanding how organisms have evolved over time. They are also used to see how life has changed throughout Earth's history. Fossils have also been used to help scientists understand how the continents appeared millions of years ago. In this investigation you will use several fossils to try to reconstruct how Earth's landmasses may have appeared approximately 250 million years ago.

Materials
- Bathymetric map
- Scissors
- tape
- 1 piece of construction paper
- Pen or pencil

 Setting up

A — Cynognathus
B — Thecodont
C — Kannemeyerid
D — Glossopteris
E — Lystrosaurus
F — Labryinthodont
G — Mesosaurus

	Fossil Name	Locations found
A	Cynognathus	South America, western Africa
B	Thecodont	Europe, eastern North America
C	Kannemeyerid	northern South America, Africa, India, Asia
D	Glossopteris	eastern South America, central Africa, India, Australia
E	Lystrosaurus	Antarctica, southern Africa, India
F	Labyrinthodont	Antarctica, central Africa, eastern Asia, Australia
G	Mesosaurus	southern South America, southern Africa

1. Using the table above and the locations each fossil has been found write the letter of each fossil onto the correct locations onto your bathymetric map. Note: the locations given in the table are only approximate locations.

2 ▶ Stop and think

a. Which of the fossils from the table were found in Antarctica? Why might this seem strange or unexpected?

b. Which of the fossils from the table were found both in North America and Asia?

c. What are some possible ways these organisms could have traveled from continent to continent when they were living?

d. If these animals and plants were not able to swim across large bodies of water such as oceans or sea explain how else the pattern of fossil distribution can be explained.

3 ▶ Doing the experiment

1. Cut out each of the following continents and landforms from your map: North America, South America, Antarctica, Africa, Europe, Australia, and Asia.
2. Place these continents onto your piece of construction paper.
3. Using the shape of the continents' coastlines and the locations where each type of fossil has been found, reconstruct the world so that all the continents are connected to form a large "supercontinent."
4. When you have completed the previous step tape down the continents to your piece of construction paper in the same positions you arranged them in step 3.

4 ▶ Thinking about what you observed

a. *Glossopteris* is an extinct type of plant referred to as a seed fern. These plants most likely thrived in tropical climates. Do any of the locations where the fossils of the glossopteris have been found seem strange? Explain your answer.

b. *Thecodont* was a small dinosaur. Where have fossils of this dinosaur been uncovered? Does it seem likely that this animal could have traveled between these two locations? Explain your answer.

c. How did the fossils of *Cynognathus* help you construct your map?

d. Where on your new map is Australia? What continents is it connected to? Which fossils did you use to help place Australia? How were they useful?

e. What other evidence might be useful for connecting the continents together into one giant landmass?

5 ▶ Exploring on your own

Pick two of the organisms from the fossil list you used in this investigation. Using your school library or the internet research this organism. Write a one paragraph summary of what you found about each of these organisms. Your research should include but is not limited to - when it lived, what it ate, how it behaved, its size, and the habitat it lived in. Include a sketch of your organisms as well.

13A Creature Cladogram

What type of information can be used to create a cladogram?

We use systems of classification in everyday life. We classify products in a grocery store. We classify people in a phone book using their last names. Organizing a collection of information into groups makes it easier for others to understand the relationship between the objects in the collection. _Taxonomy_ is the science of grouping living things on the basis of like characteristics. Organisms are classified according to their structures and evolutionary relationships. Sometimes organisms that appear very different end up in the same group together. In this investigation, you will identify common characteristics in a group of imaginary creatures and use this information to create a _cladogram_ that shows how the creatures are related.

Materials
- Creature sheet from your teacher
- Large sheet of paper
- Colored pencils or markers

 Setting up

1. Examine the sheet of the imaginary creatures. Compare and contrast the major features of the creatures.

2. Make a list in Table 1 of the different features of the animals that may provide a way to classify them into different groups.

Table I: Imaginary creature features

Creature number	Features
I	
2	
3	
4	
5	
6	
7	
8	
9	
I0	

 Stop and think

a. What types of features are contained in Table 1?

b. Is there a common relationship between the features that you identified in Table 1?

3 ▸ Doing the experiment

1. Examine the imaginary creatures. Which creatures live on land? Which creatures live in water? Record the letter of the creature in Table 2.

Table 2: Classification data

Classification	Feature	Imaginary creature number
Habitat	Land	
	Water	
Appendage	Wheels	
	Fins	
	Feet	
Body Covering	Skin	
	Scales	
	Hair	
Appendage Number	2	
	4	
	6	
	8	
	14	
Skeletal Features	Horns or Spike	
	Antennae	
	Back Ridge	
	None	

2. Examine the imaginary creatures. Which animals use wheels for locomotion? Fins? Feet? Record your answers in Table 2.

3. Examine the imaginary creatures. Which creatures are covered in skin? Scales? Hair? Record your answers in Table 2.

4. Examine the imaginary creatures. Which creatures have 2 appendages? 4? 6? Record your answers in Table 2.

5. Examine the imaginary creatures. Which creatures have horns coming from the head? Antennae? Spikes? Do any have a Back Ridge? Record you answers in Table 2.

4 Applying your knowledge

a. Based on your answers in Table 2, which creatures are most closely related?

b. Which creatures are the most distantly related?

c. Using your information in Table 2 create a _**cladogram**_ that illustrates relationships among your creatures. An example cladogram is shown to the right. Your cladogram will look much different than the one shown. It may resemble a tree with many branches. Be creative!

d. Choose a point on your diagram where two organisms branch. Describe what their common ancestor may look like. Be creative!

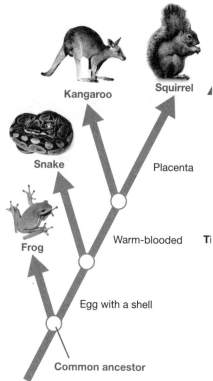

5 Exploring on your own

Once you have completed the investigation, pick one creature and using the information collected above, write a brief description of the creature's habitat, food, and predators. The goal of this activity is to be creative and use as much information as you can in describing the habitat of this creature.

13B Bread Mold

What is mold and how does it grow on bread?

Fungi are found all around you. Examples include baker's yeast, mushrooms and common bread mold. Mold grows from spores that can be found almost anywhere. The spores, under the right conditions, grow and give rise to the fuzzy organisms that are observed on week old bread left on the countertop. Most of us look at these organisms with disgust and quickly throw the bread in the trash! In this investigation, you will grow bread mold, examine the colonies.

Materials

- Homemade bread (without preservatives)
- Paper towels
- Water
- Plastic bags
- Marker
- Magnifying glass
- Microscope slides
- Distilled water
- Tweezers
- Coverslips
- Microscope

1 ▲ Setting up

1. Remove a single slice of bread and place it in a plastic bag.
2. Wet a piece of paper towel with tap water and place the wet paper towel into the plastic bag.
3. Secure the plastic bag containing the paper towel and the bread.
4. Label the plastic bag with your initials.
5. Place the bag in a designated area of the room.

2 ▲ Stop and think

a. What type(s) of organism(s) do you think will grow on the bread?

b. What information will you need if you want to classify the type of organism(s) that grow?

3 ▲ Doing the experiment

1. Remove the bread from the plastic bag and examine the bread with a magnifying glass.
2. Record your observations in Table 1.
3. Repeat Steps 1 and 2 until you begin to see organisms growing on the bread.

Table 1: Bread mold observations

Date	Observations

4. Once you observe organisms with the magnifying glass, you may want to look at these organisms with your microscope.

5. Place a single drop of water on a clean microscope slide.

6. Using the tweezers, remove a small sample of your organism and place it into the drop of water.

7. Gently place a coverslip on top of the drop of water and examine the slide under your microscope. Remember, always look at your sample under low power first and then move to a high power objective.

8. In Table 2, make a sketch of your observations.

Table 2: Microscopic evaluation of mold growth

Date	Observations

 Thinking about what you observed

a. What type of organisms did you observe growing on your bread?

b. Why is it important to use homemade bread?

c. What is the best way to keep foods free from mold?

d. What other foods do you think would grow mold if left exposed?

 Exploring on your own

This investigation can be used as a stepping stone for asking more questions about mold growth. For example, do they grow better in the dark or light? Does a certain type of bread work better than others? Design an experiment that explores one of these questions, or think of other questions you and your classmates could explore.

14A Leaf Structure and Function

What are the structures that make up a leaf and how do they function?

In most vascular plants, leaves are the principal organs for photosynthesis. Although leaves vary in their shapes and sizes, most have a thin, flat blade and veins. Some of the variation in leaf structure is related to habitat. Aquatic leaves and leaves of dry habitats have special modifications to permit survival in those different habitats. Leaf shapes, margins, and vein patterns are characteristics used to identify different species of flowering plants. In this investigation, you will identify the structures in a leaf and learn their functions.

> **Materials**
> - Leaf cutaway slide
> - Microscope
> - *Zebrina* plant
> - Microscope slide and coverslip
> - Forceps
> - Glucose solution
> - Distilled water
> - Droppers
> - Colored pencils for sketching

 Leaf structure and function

1. Obtain a microscope and leaf cutaway slide from your teacher.

2. Examine the slide under medium power. Identify the structures using the graphic below as a guide:

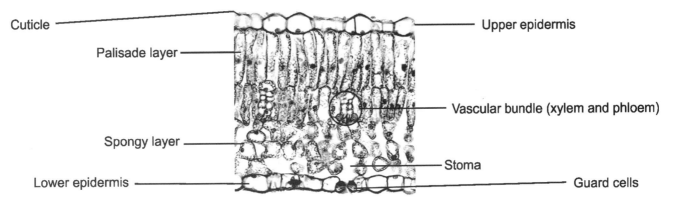

3. Sketch your leaf cutaway and label the parts you identify. Try to get them all!

4. Complete Table 1 by matching the leaf structure to its function. You may use your textbook as a hint.

Table I: Matching structures to their function

Leaf structure	Function
1. Stomata	A. Light can easily pass through this layer
2. Xylem	B. Open and close the stomata
3. Upper epidermis	C. Where most of the photosynthesis takes place
4. Guard cells	D. Transports carbon compounds like sugars
5. Phloem	E. Waxy layer that protects the leaf surface
6. Palisade layer	F. Pores that allow carbon dioxide to pass into the leaf
7. Cuticle	G. Transports water and dissolved nutrients
8. Spongy layer	H. Air space between cells allow carbon dioxide to pass through

2 ◣ Stop and think

a. Most of the structures in a leaf are related to a process. What is that process called?

b. To a leaf, what is the advantage to being thin?

c. Why do the stomata need to be able to open or close?

3 ◣ Observing stomata

1. Cut a portion of a leaf from a Zebrina plant.
2. With your fingernail or forceps, peel a portion of the lower epidermis from the leaf, starting at the cut edge. The lower epidermis is purple-pigmented, while the upper epidermis is silver and green-striped.
3. Place a drop of water on the slide. Gently lower the peel, outer side up, in the drop of water. Try to lay the peel flat on the microscope slide. Wrinkled portions have too many layers of cells and tend to trap air bubbles. Place a cover slip on top of the peel.
4. Observe your slide with your microscope. Locate the guard cells under low power.
5. When you find the guard cells, observe a stoma under medium power.

4 ◣ Stop and think

a. Can you see the chloroplasts in the guard cells?

b. What is the shape of the guard cells? Note the thickness of the inner walls of the guard cells. Are any of the stomata open?

c. Recall from your observation of the prepared slide of a leaf that a stoma opens into an air space of the spongy layer. How does this arrangement help the process of photosynthesis?

d. If the plant has been given plenty of water and looks healthy, do you think the stomata will be open or closed?

e. What would happen if a plant could not close the stomata?

f. *Why* does the carbon dioxide enter the plant? (HINT: Think about what you learned in Chapter 6 about diffusion and concentration gradients.)

5 ◣ Going further

1. Remove the coverslip. Use a tissue to remove as much of the water as you can. Now add a drop of glucose solution.
2. Place the coverslip onto the leaf and examine the stomata under medium power.

a. Did the appearance of the stomata change? How did they change?

b. What caused the change in appearance of the stomata? (HINT: review osmosis in Chapter 6 of your text.)

14B Flower Dissection

How does the design of flower help in its pollination?

Do you know where the saying "the birds and the bees" came from? It all started with flowers. Plants require pollinators like birds and bees to carry their pollen to fertilize other flowers. Without the pollen, flowers would not be able to create seeds for reproducing. An adaptation is an advantage in the physical design or behavior of an organism. An adaptation helps the organism to survive or reproduce. In this investigation, you will examine flowers to determine how they may have adaptations that increase their chances of pollination.

Materials
- Large flower
- Dissecting scissors
- Hand lens
- Metric ruler
- Microscope
- Slide
- Cover slip
- Water
- Plastic dropper
- Newspaper

 Setting up

A flower's only purpose is reproduction for the plant. In addition to male and female parts, flowers have petals and sepals. Do the sepal and petals help with pollination? Let's find out. Open a sheet of newspaper. This will be your work area. Lay the flower on the newspaper. Make a detailed sketch of what you see and record any observations in the spaces provided. Pay close attention to the color, smell, shape, and feel of the flower.

2 Stop and think

a. A *quantitative* observation is an observation that deals with a number or an amount. What quantitative observations can you make about the rest of the flower?

b. Several groups are dissecting flowers. Each of the flowers should be approximately the same age if the groups are to share their results. Why might age be an important control variable for a lab on reproduction?

c. Make a hypothesis stating ways the flower may be designed to help in pollination. Use what you know about flowers and the birds or bees that pollinate them.

3 ▲ Removing the Sepal and Petals

1. Record the number and color of the sepals in Table 1.

2. Gently pull the sepals away from the flower. If necessary, use dissecting scissors to cut away the sepals. Always cut away from yourself. Cut carefully so the structures underneath are not damaged.

3. Record the number and color of the petals in Table 1.

4. Gently pull back each of the petals revealing the male and female parts inside.

5. In the box provided, draw what you see. Label an *anther*, a *filament*, the *stigma*, the *style*, and the *ovary*. Also label the entire *pistil* and *stamen*.

4 ▲ Examining the male parts of the flower

1. Use the scissors to cut off all of the stamens. Record the number and color of the stamens in Table 1.

2. At random, select three stamens. Measure the length, in mm, of each of the three stamens. Record your results in Table 2 and calculate the average.

3. Collect a slide. Tap the stamen over the slide so that the pollen falls onto the slide. Add a drop of water to the slide and place a cover slip over the water and pollen.

4. Place the pollen slide on the microscope stage and observe the pollen grain under low power, medium power, and high power. Make a detailed sketch of one pollen grain at the highest power. Sketch the drawing in the space provided.

5. Estimate the number of pollen on one anther. Record the estimated number and color of the pollen grain in Table 1.

80

5 Examining the female parts of the flower

1. Record the number and color of the pistil in Table 1.
2. Use the scissors to carefully cut away the pistil. Attempt to cut the pistil as close as you can to its base.
3. Measure the length, in mm, of the pistil and record your results in Data Table 2.
4. Examine the overall appearance of the pistil and note any unique qualities.
5. Firmly hold the pistil flat on the newspaper. Use the edge of your scissors to cut across the ovary exposing the inside compartments.

6. Use the hand lens to examine the ovary. Estimate and record the number and color of the ovules in Table 1.

Table 1: Number and color of the flower structure

Flower Structure	Number	Color
Sepals		
Petals		
Stamen		
Pollen Grains	Estimate:	
Pistil		
Ovules	Estimate:	

Table 2: Length of the stamen and pistil measured in mm

Flower	#1	#2	#3	Average
Stamen				
Pistil				

Thinking about what you observed

a. What aspects about the overall flower shape, color, smell, size, or position, help attract pollinators?

b. What is the benefit to the plant if the flower attracts a pollinator?

c. There are several stamens and only one pistil. What might be the reasoning for this design?

d. Compare the length of your pistil to the average length of the stamen. Why would one be longer than the other?

e. Explain the process of a bee pollinating a flower.

 Exploring on your own

- After the female parts of the flower are pollinated, it may develop into fruit. Obtain a piece of fruit. Try to match parts of the fruit to parts of the flower from which they developed.

Or

- Different flowers are designed for different pollinators. For example, some flowers are pollinated by bees. Others are pollinated by the wind. Would a flower have any major differences because of the type of pollinator? Design an experiment to find the answer. Check in with your teacher before carrying out your investigation.

15A Observing Planarians

What are the structures and behaviors of planarians?

Planarians are invertebrate animals belonging to the *Phylum Platyhelminthes* (flatworms). You can easily find planarians on your own. Shake pond weeds into a pan or turn over stream rocks and look carefully at the rock surfaces. You can also collect flatworms on your own. Put a small pellet of canned pet food in an old nylon stocking. Secure that bag in a stream bed or pond shore overnight. In the morning you may find a collection of flatworms crawling over the bag! In this investigation, you will observe planarians and identify their structures and behavior. You will also design and conduct a few experiments.

Materials
- Live planarians
- Petri dish
- Spring water
- Plastic spoon
- Flashlight
- Paper bag
- Magnifying glass
- Microscope
- Depression slide and coverslip
- Food for planaria
- Pipette

1 Observing your planarian

1. You will receive a small petri dish with a flatworm inside it. The flatworm is the freshwater planarian, also known as *Dugesia*. Record all of your answers and data for Part 1 in Table 1.

2. List 3 characteristics of flatworms.

3. What type of *symmetry* does this worm have? The term symmetry refers to the body plan of the organism. Use the diagram below to answer.

Types of symmetry — Asymmetrical, Radial, Bilateral

4. Using the plastic spoon, carefully move your planarian into a depression slide containing a few drops of spring water.

5. Observe your worm using a microscope. Sketch the planarian. Label the eyespots. Label the *anterior* (front) and *posterior* (rear) ends.

6. Carefully transfer your worm back to its petri dish.

7. Measure your planarian. You can do this by removing some of the water from the dish and waiting for the worm to stretch out. Measure the length of the worm in millimeters. Always replace the water. You can use the dish lid to transfer water to and from the planarian environment.

8. Write your length on the board. When all the lengths are written down, determine the average planarian length.

Table 1: Planarian observations

Characteristics of flatworms:	
a.	
b.	
c.	
Type of symmetry:	
Sketch:	
Length of your planarian (mm):	Average length of planarians (mm):

2 ▲ Observing behavior and feeding

1. Observe the planarian for five minutes. Does the planarian seem active or passive? How does it move? Does it swim or creep? Record your observations in Table 2.

2. Where in the dish does your planarian spend most of its time? Record your observations in Table 2.

3. Make a current in the water with a pipette. How does the planarian react? Record your observations in Table 2.

Table 2: Planaria movement and behavior

Movement	
Location preference	
Reaction to current	

4. Like you, planarians display the behavior of being right or left handed. You can discover whether your worm is right or left handed by flipping the planarian over on its *dorsal* surface (back) and seeing which direction it flips to turn back over. If it rolls to the right, it is right handed, if it rolls to the left, it is left handed. Do five trials to determine the handedness of your planarian. Fill out Table 3. Compare your results to others in your class.

Table 3: Planaria "handedness"

Trial 1	
Trial 2	
Trial 3	
Trial 4	
Trial 5	
Based on your trials, is your planarian right or left-handed?	

84

5. Your teacher will give you a piece of food for your planarian. Drop the piece of food into the petri dish with the planarian. Observe the planarian's reactions. It may take a few minutes.   How does it eat the food?   Where is its mouth? What is the name of the tube used for feeding in the planarian? You may look this up in your textbook. Record your observations in Table 4.

Table 4: Feeding

How does the planarian react to food?	
How does the planarian eat?	
Where is its mouth located?	
What is the name of the tube used for feeding?	

3 ▲ Investigating on your own

a. Design an experiment to test the planarian's reaction to light and dark. You will have flashlights and the room will be darkened for this part of the investigation. First, state your hypothesis.

b. Describe your design for the experiment.

c. Conduct your experiment to determine whether the planarian prefers light or dark. Construct a data table and record your observations and data.

d. Write your conclusions. Make sure you state whether your conclusion supports or refutes your hypothesis. Include your reasoning.

4 ▲ Exploring further

a. If time permits, you can explore how planarians reproduce. Planarians are hermaphrodites. Define *hermaphrodite*.

b. Planarians can also reproduce by regeneration. Define *regeneration*. Is this method of reproduction sexual or asexual?

To do the experiment:

1. Ask your teacher for another planarian.
2. Pour out some of the water, so that the planarian is mostly un-submerged. Call your teacher over and ask to have your planarian cut in half. Observe the two pieces of the planarian under the microscope.
3. Label the lid with your NAME and HOUR.
4. Make a prediction: How long do you think (in days) will it take for your planarian to completely regenerate?

15B The Mammalian Eye

What are the structures of the mammalian eye and how do they function?

The mammalian eye is an amazing organ. It consists of many specialized cells and tissues that make up several different structures. The structures have certain functions and together, they form images that are interpreted by the brain. In this investigation, you identify the most important structures of a sheep eye and learn their functions.

Materials

• Preserved sheep's eye	• Vinyl or latex gloves
• Forceps	• Apron
• Dissection probes	• Goggles
• Dissection scissors	• Paper towels
• Dissection tray	• Plastic trash bag

Safety tip: wear gloves, apron, and safety goggles during the investigation.

WARNING — This lab contains chemicals that may be harmful if misused. Read cautions on individual containers carefully. Not to be used by children except under adult supervision.

 Setting up

1. Put on your gloves, apron, and safety goggles.

2. Your teacher will give your group a preserved sheep eye in a dissection tray. Handle the sheep eye with care. The chemicals used to preserve it may be toxic.

3. Obtain a dissecting kit containing dissection probes, scissors, and forceps. Handle the equipment with care and do not play with it.

2 External features of the eye

1. Examine the outside layer of the sheep eye. Notice the yellow tissue surrounding the eye. This is fat tissue. Using scissors, trim any excess fat tissue from around the eye.

2. Locate the sclera, the cornea and the optic_ nerve.

3. The *sclera* is the tough outer coating of the eye. The sclera gives the eye its shape and helps to protect the delicate inner parts.

4. The *cornea* is the transparent front part of the eye. Together with the lens, the cornea

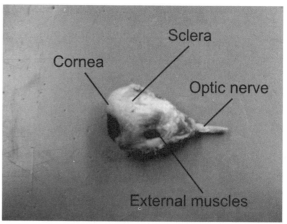

refracts light and helps the eye to focus. The cornea gives a larger contribution to the total refraction than the lens. The curvature of the cornea is fixed while that of the lens is changeable.

5. The *optic nerve* is the nerve that transmits visual information from the eye to the brain.

6. Locate the four *externally attached muscles*. These muscles control eye movement and help focus images. Identify all four muscles.

3 ▶ Stop and think

a. What is the function of the sclera, cornea, and optic nerve?

b. The human eye has six externally attached muscles instead of only four like the sheep's. Predict how a human's eye might move differently than a sheep's eye.

c. Although the muscles of each individual eye work as a team, the eyes themselves do not focus or work together until months after birth. However, one eye remains dominant. Form a circle with your thumb and index finger. Hold that position and place your hand in front of you. With both eyes, look at something through the circle. Continue to hold that position and close one eye; then open it. Close the other eye. The eye which is still able to view the object through the circle is your dominant eye. Which of your eyes is dominant?

4 ▶ Removing the cornea

1. Use the scissors to carefully cut around the junction between the cornea and the sclera. Cut completely around and remove the cornea.

2. Lay the cornea on the dissecting tray. Identify the lens, iris, and pupil.

3. You will also see a clear jelly-like fluid. This is the vitreous humor. The vitreous humor is attached to the lens.

Removing the cornea

4. The *lens* is a transparent structure in the eye that, along with the cornea, helps to refract and focus light. A ring of tiny *ciliary muscles*, located along the inner side of the iris, connects the lens to the middle layer of the eye. Ciliary muscles contract to change the curvature of the lens.

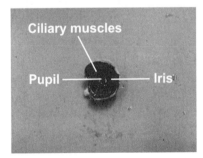

5. The *iris* is the pigmented part of the eye and helps to change the size of the pupil.

6. The *pupil* is a hole in the iris. The iris opens or closes to control the amount of light entering the pupil. The pupil gets smaller in bright light and larger in dim light.

7. Remove lens to look at it. In a living organism, it is completely transparent. To focus on closer objects, it gets fatter so it can refract more light.

The lens

5 ▶ Stop and think

a. What is the function of the lens, iris, and pupil?

b. If you enter a very bright room after being in the dark, what would happen to your pupils?

6   Cutting the eye in half

1. Carefully insert the dissecting scissors at the top of the eye where you removed the cornea.

2. Following a circular pattern around the sclera, rotate the eye while continuing to carefully cut the eye in half.

3. Carefully open and separate the front from the back of the eye without damaging its internal structures.

4. Cutting the sclera in a circular pattern resulted in also cutting the thin reflective middle layer lining of the sheep eye. This colorful reflective lining is called the *tapetum* and is not found in the human eye. The tapetum is an adaptation for seeing better in the dark.

5. Observe a wrinkled sac-like structure attached to the optic nerve and connected to the back of the eye. This is the retina. It is the inmost layer of the eye. The <u>*retina*</u> is a thin layer of cells at the back of the eye of vertebrates. It is the part of the eye that converts light into nerve signals. The point at which the retina tissue connects to the optic nerve is the eye's blind spot.

6. Separate the retina from the back portion of the eye and again observe the colorful reflective layer of the tapetum.

7. Remove the tapetum from the tough, outer layer of the sclera to expose the choroid. The <u>*choroid*</u> is the layer of the eye lying between the retina and the sclera. The choroid provides oxygen and nourishment to the outer layers of the retina.

The eye cut in half

Tapetum

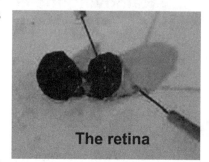

The retina

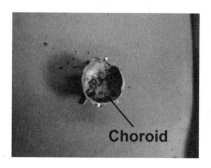

Choroid

7   Cleaning up

1. Wrap the sheep eye and its parts in many layers of paper towels.

2. Properly dispose of the paper towel containing the sheep eye in the plastic trash bag your teacher brings around.

3. Thoroughly clean all dissecting tools with soap and water.

4. Dispose of all used vinyl gloves in a plastic trash bag.

5. Wash down all lab areas with soap and water.

6. Thoroughly wash your hands with warm water and soap.

8 ▲ Applying your knowledge

a.   Match each structure of the sheep eye with its function.

Table 1: Structures of the eye and their functions

Eye structure	Function
1. External muscles	A. A clear structure that refracts light and can change in curvature
2. Retina	B. Provides oxygen and nourishment to the outer layers of the retina
3. Cornea	C. A tiny ring of muscles that change the shape of the lens
4. Lens	D. The pigmented ring of muscles that change the size of the pupil
5. Optic nerve	E. Works with the lens to refract light and helps the eye to focus
6. Iris	F. Move the eye around
7. Sclera	G. Transmits signals from the eye to the brain
8. Ciliary muscles	H. Gives the eye its shape and protects the inner parts
9. Choroid	I. A thin layer of cells that convert light into nerve signals

b.   Name two differences between the sheep eye and the human eye.

c.   Why does the optic nerve cause a blind spot?

d.   To find your blind spot, use the two dots below. Hold one hand over your left eye, look directly at the left-hand dot. At first, you can see both dots even though you're looking directly at only one. As you slowly move the page closer to your eyes, the right-hand dot disappears! If you move your eye, the dot will reappear, but as long as you focus on the first dot, the second will be invisible. Move even closer and the missing dot reappears. You've found your blind spot!

●   ●

16A Who's Got the Beat?

How fast will your pulse increase with physical activity?

Unlike most workers, the heart never gets time off. Each hour, an average heart pumps about 75 gallons of blood throughout your body. Even more difficult, during exercise the heart must work overtime. The heart is the pump that causes your blood to circulate throughout your body and to all of your cells. The heart makes sure that the oxygen you breathe, the nutrients from the food you eat, and the water you drink, get delivered to your body. Without the heart, each of your organs would not be able to function. When you exercise, you increase the demands for energy. Therefore your heart must increase the speed at which the blood delivers the vital nutrients. But just how hard is your heart willing to work? In this investigation, you will examine how much your heart rate will increase and the amount of time it takes for your heart to return to its normal rate.

> ### Materials
> - Graph Paper
> - Watch or Clock with a Second hand
> - Metric Ruler

 Setting up

A *pulse* is the vibrations created each time your heart pumps blood through your arteries. The rate of your pulse indicates the speed of your heart pumping. You will work with a partner to find your pulse. Follow the steps below to find the pulse in the wrist.

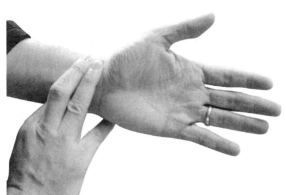

1. Find a large tendon on the underside of your wrist. Using your middle and ring finger from your other hand, locate your pulse just below the base of the thumb and on the outside of the large tendon.

2. Count the number of beats in your pulse while your partner times you for 1 minute.

3. Practice this step until you can easily find and take your pulse.

 Stop and think

a. Why can't you use your thumb or index finger to take your partners pulse?

b. Each student in your class will conduct the experiment. What should be the control variables for each student if the class is going to share their data?

c. How much faster do you think your pulse will be if you run for 1 minute? Do you think your partner's pulse will increase by the same amount?

Doing the experiment

Safety tip: caution should be taken for students for whom strenuous activity is risky.

1. Take your resting pulse rate before you exercise. Count the beats in your pulse while your partner times you for one minute. Record your results in Table 1. Repeat the step two more times, and average your results.

2. Do 50 jumping jacks. Do the jumping jacks in a row without stopping. After you stop, take your pulse for one minute.

3. Continue to take you pulse for the next four minutes without exercising again, This will determine how quickly your heart returns to its resting rate. Record the results after each minute in Table 2.

4. Switch roles and repeat steps 1-2.

Table 1: Rate of each student's pulse when resting

Individual	Beats/Minute			
	Trial 1	Trial 2	Trial 3	Average

Table 2: Rate of each student's pulse after exercising

Individual	Beats/Minute				
	1 min. after exercising	2 min. after exercising	3 min. after exercising	4 min. after exercising	5 min. after exercising

Thinking about what you observed

a. Plot each of your points from Table 2 on Graph 1 on the next page. Plot your partner's points in a different color. Use the metric ruler to create a best-fit line.

b. Extend the line to estimate your heart rate after ten minutes of resting. Using the graph, estimate how long it would take for your heart to return to its resting rate. Your resting rate is calculated in Table 1.

c. Why would it be inaccurate to continue the graph line until it hit 0?

d. What else, besides exercise, might speed up your heart rate?

e. Did you and you partner have the same results? Why might that be?

f. Why do you think your heart rate increases when you exercise?

Exploring on your own

- Your pulse can also be taken on your neck. Would the experiment turn out differently if you used the pulse on your neck instead of your wrist? Design an experiment to find out. Check with your teacher before conducting the experiment.

OR

- As we get older, does our heart rate change? Design an experiment to compare the average heart rate of individuals at different ages. Will there be a pattern? Check with your teacher before conducting the experiment.

16B The Pressure's On

How powerful is your heart? And how much does your blood pressure increase when your heart contracts?

Flexibility is important, especially if you are a blood vessel such as an artery. Every minute the average heart pumps 60 to 80 times. With each pump, the heart forces an average of sixty milliliters of blood into attached arteries to be circulated throughout your body to deliver important nutrients such as oxygen, food, and water. But just how much force is necessary with each contraction? Just how much pressure does the heart have to overcome to circulate the five liters of blood found in your body? In this investigation, you will find an answer by measuring your blood pressure when your heart is at rest, the diastolic blood pressure, and your blood pressure after your heart just pumped, systolic blood pressure. Then you will compare your results with the average statistics for your age group.

Materials

- Sphygmomanometer
- Stethoscope
- Table
- Alcohol
- Cotton swabs

WARNING — This lab contains chemicals that may be harmful if misused. Read cautions on individual containers carefully. Not to be used by children except under adult supervision.

 Setting up

A sphygmomanometer can measure the amount of pressure required to circulate your blood. When your heart pumps, your blood pressure increases. This is called *systolic blood pressure*. In between pumps, your blood pressure decreases. This is called *diastolic blood pressure*. You will measure both.

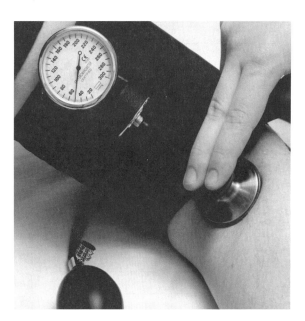

1. Sit with your partner at a table. Place your partner's arm on the table with the palm up and place the cuff of the sphygmomanometer above your partner's elbow. The cuff should be snug but loose enough to fit two fingers through.

2. Place the stethoscope in your ears. Place the round head of the stethoscope on the brachial artery on your partner's arm.

3. Make sure the valve is closed on the pump of the sphygmomanometer.

Safety tip: the sphygmomanometer should only be used under adult supervision.

Stop and think

a. Why might it be important to place the arm in a horizontal position rather than letting it hang at your side?

b. Each student in you class will conduct the experiment. What should be the control variables for each student if the class is going to share their data?

c. Develop a hypothesis. Do you think everyone's heart creates the same pressure? Explain why or why not.

 Doing the experiment:

1. Pump enough pressure to bring the needle on the gauge of the sphygmomanometer to 180. Now the pressure from the cuff is greater than the blood pressure so no blood will be able to flow through the artery.

2. Slowly open the valve on the pump, watch the gauge, and listen for a heart beat. Once the blood pressure is greater than the pressure from the cuff, you will hear the heartbeat. This is the systolic blood pressure or the blood pressure when it is strongest because the heart has just pumped it. Record this number in Table 1.

3. Continue to listen. Watch the needle on the gauge. Note the number of the needle when you no longer hear the heartbeat. This is the diastolic blood pressure.

4. Record your partner's blood pressure. Clean the ear pieces with alcohol and trade places.

Table 1: Systolic and diastolic blood pressure

Student	Systolic Blood Pressure Measured in Millimeters of Mercury	Diastolic Blood Pressure Measured in Millimeters of Mercury
You		
Your partner		

Table 2: Average blood pressure of individuals determined by age

Age in Years	Average Systolic Pressure Measured in Millimeters of Mercury	Average Diastolic Pressure Measured in Millimeters of Mercury
Birth	70	45
5	?	?
10	105	70
15	117	77
20	120	79
25	121	80
30	122	81
35	123	82
40	125	83
45	127	84
50	129	85
55	131	86
60	134	87

Thinking about what you observed

a. Plot each of the points from Data Table 2 onto Graph 1. Plot diastolic and systolic blood pressures in different colors. Use the metric ruler to create a best-fit line.

b. What would be the systolic and diastolic blood pressure for the average 5 year old?

c. Why might the blood pressure be so low for an infant?

d. How does blood pressure change with age? Explain why this might be.

e. What can an individual do to increase his or her blood pressure?

f. What can an individual do to decrease their blood pressure?

 g. The arteries are vessels that carry blood away from the heart. Veins are blood vessels that carry blood to the heart. Would you expect the blood pressure to be greater in your arteries or in your veins? Explain why.

5 **Exploring on your own**

Does your blood pressure change with the time of day? How could you investigate this idea? Design an experiment to find out. Check with your teacher before conducting the experiment.

17A Forces in Simple Machines

How do simple machines work?

Would you believe that a small child could lift an elephant with only muscle power? It's true! You could make it possible by building a simple machine out of ropes and pulleys. In this Investigation, you will learn how to build machines that allow you to lift large weights with small forces. You will also learn how to measure the input and output forces of these machines.

> **Materials**
> - Ropes and pulleys
> - Force scales
> - Tape measure
> - Ruler
> - Physics stand

 Identifying input and output forces

Watch a demonstration of a simple machine made with ropes and pulleys.

a. What is the definition of a simple machine?

b. With your class, brainstorm additional examples of simple machines. For each machine you come up with, identify the input and output force.

 Setting up the ropes and pulleys

1. Attach four weights to the bottom block. Use a force scale to obtain the weight of the bottom block after you attach the weights and record the weight. Weight of bottom block: _____ N.

2. The output force of this simple machine will be used to lift the bottom block. Attach the top block near the top of the physics stand. The yellow string can be clipped to either the top block or the bottom block. Start with the yellow string clipped to the bottom block.

Why all the strings?

- The yellow string will be used to move the bottom pulley block with the weights up and down. You will pull on one end of the yellow string. There is a clip at the other end of the yellow string for attaching to the pulley blocks.

- The yellow string may have several strands that directly support the bottom pulley block. These are called the supporting strands.

- The pink string is the safety string. It holds up the bottom block while you rearrange the yellow string.

Safety tip: Don't pull sideways or you can tip the stand over!

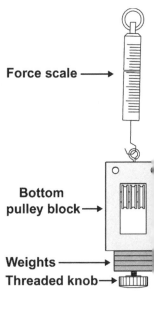

Force scale →

Bottom pulley block →

Weights →

Threaded knob →

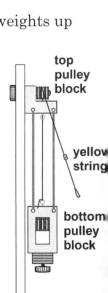

top pulley block

yellow string

bottom pulley block

3 **Investigating the ropes and pulleys**

1. Clip the end of the yellow string to the bottom pulley block. Pass the string over the middle pulley of the top block. Use the marker stop (cord stop) to hook the force scale to the string.

2. Measure the force it takes to slowly lift the bottom pulley block.

3. This arrangement has one strand supporting the bottom pulley block. Record the force in Table 1 in the row corresponding to one strand.

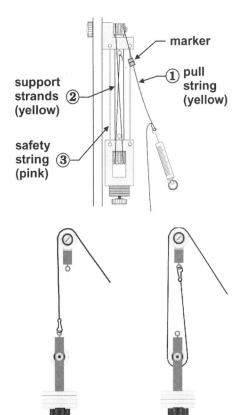

4. Take the yellow string off and clip the end to the top block next. Pass the string around the middle pulley in the bottom block and back over the middle pulley in the top block.

5. Move the marker and measure the force it takes to slowly lift the bottom pulley block. Record this force in the row for two supporting strands.

6. Rearrange the yellow strings so that you get three, four, five, and six supporting strands. Measure and record the force it takes to lift the bottom pulley block for each new setup.

This arrangement has one supporting strand

This arrangement has two supporting strands

Table 1: Number of strands and force

Number of support strands	Force to lift bottom pulley block (N)
1	
2	
3	
4	
5	
6	

a. As you add more supporting strands, what happens to the force needed to lift the bottom block?

b. How does the amount of input force required to lift the bottom block change with the string arrangement? Can you identify a mathematical rule?

4 **What did you learn?**

a. How are all simple machines alike? How is a lever different from a machine made with ropes and pulleys?

b. What is the relationship between the number of strings on the ropes and pulleys, and the amount of input force required to lift the bottom block?

17B Levers and the Human Body

How does a lever work? What types of levers does your body have?

How can you lift up a car—or even an elephant—all by yourself? One way is with a lever. The lever is an example of a simple machine.

Materials
- Lever
- Physics stand
- Force scales
- Weights

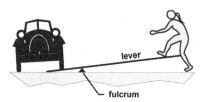

 Setting up the lever

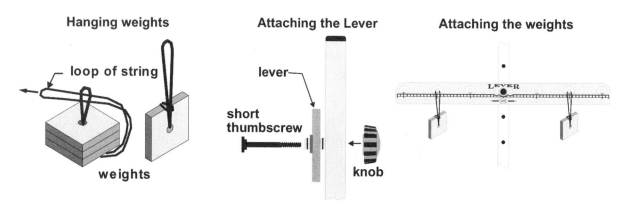

1. Use loops of string to make hangers for the weights. You can put more than one weight on a single string.

2. The weights can be hung from the lever by hooking the string over the center peg in the holes. Make sure that the string is all the way around the peg!

 Levers in equilibrium

a. The lever is in equilibrium when all the weights on one side balance all the weights on the other side. Hang the weights as shown below. Does the lever balance?

b. What variables can be changed to balance a lever?

c. On the diagram below label the fulcrum, the input arm and the output arm.

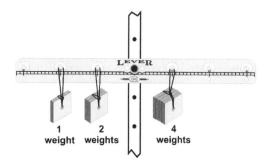

3 **Trying different combinations to balance the lever**

Make different combinations of weights and positions that balance. Use the chart below to write down the numbers of weights you put in each position. If you want to conduct more than four trials, write your results on a separate sheet of paper

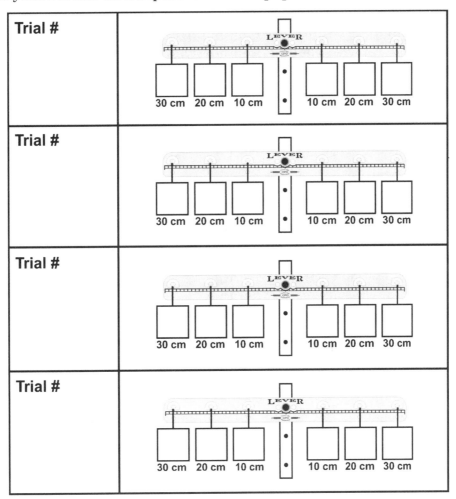

 4 **Determine the mathematical rule for equilibrium**

Using the data in the chart above, determine a mathematical rule for levers in equilibrium. Think about the variables in the experiment: *input force*, *output force*, *length of input arm*, and *length of output arm*. First, make some calculations, then write your rule as an equation.

 5 **What did you learn?**

a.   Draw a lever and label these parts: fulcrum, input arm, output arm, input force, and output force.

b.   There are two ratios that can be used to determine mechanical advantage in levers. What are the two equations? What is the relationship between the two equations?

c.   In a lever, you can increase the amount of output force by increasing the length of the input arm. When you do this, what must decrease in order to increase output force?

6 The human body

Arms, legs, fingers, toes, the jaw, even the head and neck work like levers. Contracting and extending muscles provide the force to move our levers. Our joints are the fulcrums around which these levers pivot and move. Our bones are the levers themselves. Lets take a look at the human arm and examine how it works like a lever.

Let your left arm hang down by your side. Place the hand of your right arm into the inner part of your elbow. Slowly lift your left arm (palm up) until it is level with the floor. Feel that tissue in your elbow tightening up with your right hand? That is the connective tissue that joins your biceps muscle to the bones of your forearm, the radius and ulna. We can use the physics stand and the lever to make a model of the human arm and measure the forces involved when we lift something.

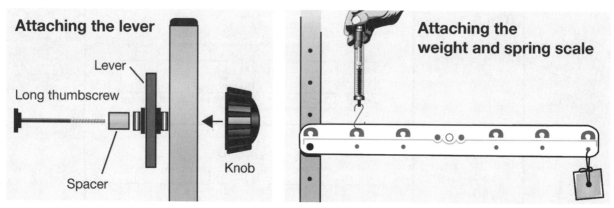

Use what you have learned about lever terms in the first part of the investigation to record your answers in the appropriate columns in Table 1. You will need to include units for each entry you record.

1. Attach the lever to the stand, but this time use the hole on the left-most side of the lever. Use one of the short thumbscrews. Do not tighten the knob all the way. Leave a little room so the lever can still pivot.

2. Use a loop of string to hang one weight on the right-most side of the lever. Measure its weight in newtons using a force scale (the green one). Record it in Table 1.

3. Measure this distance from the pivot point to the position of the hanging weight and record it in Table 1

4. Measure the distance from the pivot point to the next hole on the lever. This is where we will apply force to lift the lever. Record the distance in Table 1.

Table 1: Input and output data

Output force (N)	Input arm (cm)	Output arm (cm)	Mechanical advantage	Predicted input force (N)	Measured output force (N)

100

7 The lever arm model

a. Calculate the mechanical advantage of the lever. Record your result in Table 1.

b. Based on the mechanical advantage, predict the force required to lift the lever up and keep it horizontal. Record it in Table 1.

c. The connective tissue in your arm attaches your biceps to your forearm at the inside of the elbow. Since the muscle provides the lifting force close to the elbow joint, we will provide the lifting force for the lever close to the pivot point. Hook a force scale (the red one) to the lever at the hole just to the right of the pivot point and lift up until the lever is horizontal. Keep it horizontal and record the force needed to keep it there in Table 1.

d. How does your predicted value match your measured value? Why do you think this is?

e. Test your reason why the values are different. What did you find?

f. Draw a diagram showing how the lever setup models an arm lifting a weight.

18A Color Vision

How do our eyes see color?

Light is so useful and common that we often don't think about what light is. Light has many properties, such as its ability to carry images, colors, and heat. This Investigation will examine some of the properties of light related to its color.

Materials

- Light and Optics Kit
- Room that may be darkened
- TV or computer screen

 Sources of light

a. What color shirt are you wearing? What do you think gives your shirt this color?

b. How do you think light is involved with the color of your shirt?

c. Can you see your shirt in the dark? What does this tell you about whether or not your shirt creates its own light?

d. Where do you think the light that traveled from your shirt to your eyes came from?

e. Can you see a TV or a computer screen in the dark? Turn one on and try it. What does this tell you about whether or not the TV or computer screen creates its own light?

f. How is the TV or computer screen's light different from the light that comes from your shirt?

How do we see colors?

Brown hair

Red ice pop

Yellow shirt (with red spots!)

Red shorts with yellow flowers

Give off light or reflect light?

?

Can you see a TV in a completely dark room?

2 ► Making colors with light

1. Plug the red, green, and blue LED lamps into the optics table.

2. Place the three lamps side by side on one edge of the optics table. Set one of the lenses in the middle. Set the screen (back of the mirror) at the opposite edge from the LEDs.

3. You should see three spots of color on the screen (red-green-blue). Move the lens and screen to make the three spots overlap and observe the colors on the screen.

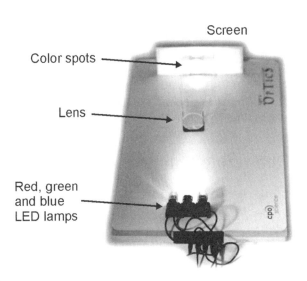

3 ► Thinking about what you observed

a. What color do you see when you mix red and green light?

b. What color do you see when you mix red and blue light?

c. What color do you see when you mix blue and green light?

d. What color is produced when all three colors of light are equally mixed?

Table 1: Mixing primary colors of light

LED color combination	Color you see
Red + Green	
Green + Blue	
Blue + Red	
Red + Green + Blue	

18B The Human Eye

How does the human eye form an image?

Everything we have learned about light can be used to understand how the human eye sees. The eye works together with the optic nerve and your brain to help you see images. By focusing light onto specialized light sensitive cells, we are able to see the world around us.

Materials
- Light and Optics set

Refracting light through a lens

Lenses are able to bend light rays so they come to a point called the *focal point*. This bending of the light rays is called refraction. You are going to use a laser to make a ray diagram to find the focal point of a lens.

1. Fix a sheet of graph paper to the optics table with a magnetic strip.

2. Set the laser so the back is tipped up on the magnetic strip and the beam is pointed down slightly at the paper. Align the laser so the beam follows a horizontal grid line straight across the paper.

3. Set the large flat lens on the paper and center it on the beam as shown in the diagram. Trace the shape of the lens on the graph paper. If you move the lens, you can easily put it back on its traced shape now.

4. Draw lines following the beam as it leaves the laser, enters the lens, and then exits the lens. Point the laser so it always follows one of the grid lines across the paper on its way to the lens.

5. Make a dot under the laser exactly where the beam starts and make another where it enters the lens. Do the same where the beam exits the lens and put another close to the edge where the beam goes off the paper. Connect the dots to mark the path of the beam.

6. After you have marked the path of the beam through the center of the lens, move the laser to different parallel grid lines above and below the center of the lens. Mark two beam paths above and two paths below the center path.

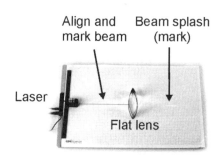

Align and mark beam / Beam splash (mark) / Laser / Flat lens

Move laser and align with a lower grid line

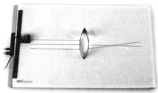

Move laser and align with an upper grid line

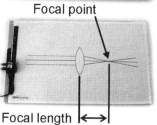

Completed ray diagram / Focal point / Focal length

2 ▸ Thinking about what you observed

a. Describe the path of the laser beam as it travels away from the laser and through the lens.

b. What is the focal point of a lens? Mark the focal point on the ray diagram you just drew.

c. What is the focal length of a lens? Measure the focal length of the flat glass lens from the ray diagram.

3 ▸ Making an image with a lens

1. Find a wall at least 5 meters away from a lamp or sunlit window. Tape a piece of white paper to the wall to create a screen for seeing the image.

2. Get one of the round convex glass lenses in the metal holders. Move the lens toward and away from the screen until you get a sharp image of the lamp or window. Try distances between 10 and 20 centimeters away from your screen.

3. Use this technique and measure the distance from the lens to the screen to determine the image distance for both lenses (Table 1).

Table 1: Image distance and focal lengths of lenses

	Image distance (mm)	predicted focal length (mm)	actual focal length (mm)
White Lens			
Black lens			

Now that you have seen the lenses create images, how do you think image distance is related to focal length?

1. Based on what you have learned about focal length, predict the focal lengths of the white and black lenses in Table 1.

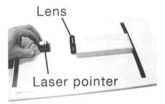

2. Now its time to check your predictions. Place the wooden block flat on the optics board with the graph paper side up and shine the laser at it so the beam splashes across the wooden block.

3. Line the block up with the graph paper and put one of the lenses on the optics board so the beam goes through the lens and still splashes across the wooden block graph paper.

4. We will use two beams to find the focal length. One beam will pass through the left edge of the lens, and one on the right. Once again, you will line the laser up on the graph paper and shine it perpendicular to the lens.

5. Use the dry erase marker to mark the path of the two beams. Measure the distance from the surface of the lens to where the two paths cross to find the focal length of one lens and record it in Table 1. Erase the marks once you have recorded your data and try the other lens. Repeat steps 1-5 and record your data.

4 ▲ Thinking about what you observed

a. What did you find happened to the light rays as they passed through the lens?

b. How did your focal length predictions compare to your measured values?

c. How is the image distance related to the focal length of each lens?

5 ▲ Projecting an image with a lens.

Red or blue
LED lamp

Lens

1. The red and blue LED lamps each have a letter F engraved on the front face. Take either color and place it near one edge of the optics table.

2. Take the white or black lens and set it on the optics table about 20 cm away from the LED lamp so the light shines through the lens. Think about our previous activities and predict the distance the lens will need to be from the LED to project a sharp, in-focus image of the letter "F" onto the wall. Record your prediction in Table 2.

3. Place the wooden block under the optics board on the opposite side from the light. This will tilt the optics table up and the LED will be aimed up onto the wall of your classroom.

4. Move the lens toward and away from the LED until you can see a sharp image of the letter "F" on the wall. Once the image is in focus measure the distance from the LED to the lens and record it in Table 2. Look at the letter "F" and record its characteristics in Table 2.

5. Repeat the activity with the other lens.

Table 2: Lens distance and characteristics of image

	Predicted lens distance (mm)	Measured lens distance (mm)	Larger or smaller?	Right-side-up or up-side-down?
White Lens				
Black lens				

6 ▲ Thinking about what you observed

a. Describe the characteristics of the images formed by the lenses. Characteristics include whether the images are larger, smaller, right-side-up, or up-side-down.

b. How is the focal length of a lens related to the lens distance required to project a sharp, in-focus image?

c. How did your lens distance predictions compare to your measured values?

d. Discuss with your class how projecting an image with a lens (the letter "F" on the wall) is similar to making an image with a lens (the image of the window on a screen).

Parts of the eye

In the diagram to the right find the following parts;

1. Cornea
2. Iris
3. Lens
4. Retina
5. Optic nerve

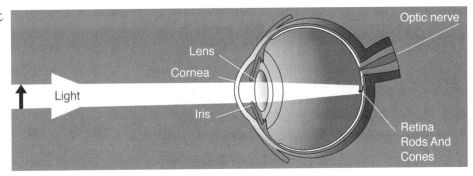

We are going to look at all of the parts of the eye and find out what they do.

 The cornea

Look at the shape and location of the cornea in the diagram above.

a. Where is the cornea located?

b. What shape is the cornea?

c. Based on its location and shape what do you think is the function of the cornea?

d. What effect on light entering the eye do you think the cornea has?

 The iris

The iris is the colored ring that surrounds the black spot on the eye, called the pupil. The iris can change its size, making the pupil larger or smaller.

a. Where is the iris located?

b. What is the shape of the iris?

c. Based on its location and shape what do you think is the function of the iris?

d. What effect on light entering the eye do you think the iris has?

e. Why do you think some animals (like cats) have differently shaped irises?

10 **The lens**

You used lenses in the investigation that were shaped very much like the lens of the eye. There is one big difference: the lens in the eye can change its shape!

a. Think back to using the black and white lenses. Did they have the same focal length?

b. What do you think happens to the focal length of the eye's lens when it changes its shape?

c. Below are four diagrams showing light coming from the left and traveling to the right (see the arrows) through the lens. Draw in how you think light would refract through these different shaped lenses;

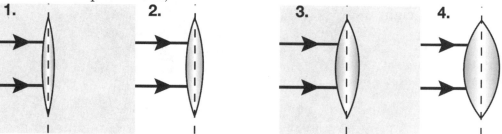

d. Why do you think the lens of your eye would need to change its shape?

e. How would the distance of the object being looked at effect the shape of the lens?

11 The retina

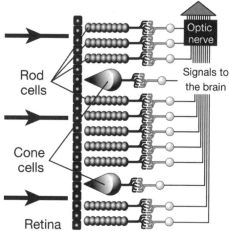

All parts of the eye work together to control the amount of light entering the eye and focus an image on a small light sensitive area of specialized tissue at the back of the eye called the retina. The *retina* detects light and transmits the visual information to the optic nerve and onto the brain.

Light sensitive cells in the eye are called *photoreceptors*. There are two different kinds of photoreceptors in the retina, *rod cells* and *cone cells*.

Rod cells are sensitive to the intensity of light. They see in black white and shades of grey. Rod cells are many times more sensitive to light than cone cells.

Enlargement of retinal tissue

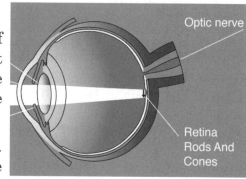

Cone cells are sensitive to color. There are three kinds of cone cells. One kind responds most strongly to red light. A second kind responds most strongly to green light. The third kind responds most strongly to blue light. All the colors you can see are combinations of signals from all three kinds of cone cells. For example, yellow is seen when both the red and green cone cells send signals to the brain.

Signals from all photoreceptors complete with light intensity and all detected colors are sent to the brain and assembled as the image we see as a mosaic of millions of tiny dots.

12 Putting it all together

a. Describe the process of how the eye allows an image to be seen.

b. How would you describe the image seen by an animal that has very few or no cone cells?

c. For what reason do you think an animal would have excess rod cells?

d. For what reason do you think an animal would have excess cone cells?

Lab Skills and Equipment Setups

LAB SKILLS

SETUP

Safety Skills

What can I do to protect myself and others in the lab?

Science equipment and supplies are fun to use. However, these materials must always be used with care. Here you will learn how to be safe in a science lab.

Materials
• Poster board
• Felt-tip markers

 Follow these basic safety guidelines

Your teacher will divide the class into groups. Each group should create a poster-sized display of one of the following guidelines. Hang the posters in the lab. Review these safety guidelines before each Investigation.

1. **Prepare** for each Investigation.

   a. Read the Investigation sheets carefully.

   b. Take special note of safety instructions.

2. **Listen** to your teacher's instructions before, during, and after the Investigation. Take notes to help you remember what your teacher has said.

3. **Get ready to work:** Roll long sleeves above the wrist. Tie back long hair. Remove dangling jewelry and any loose, bulky outer layers of clothing. Wear shoes that cover the toes.

4. **Gather** protective clothing (goggles, apron, gloves) at the beginning of the Investigation.

5. **Emphasize teamwork.** Help each other. Watch out for one another's safety.

6. **Clean up** spills immediately. Clean up all materials and supplies after an Investigation.

 Know what to do when...

1. **working with heat.**

   a. Always handle hot items with a hot pad. Never use your bare hands.

   b. Move carefully when you are near hot items. Sudden movements could cause burns if you touch or spill something hot.

   c. Inform others if they are near hot items or liquids

2. **working with electricity.**

   a. Always keep electric cords away from water.

   b. Extension cords must not be placed where they may cause someone to trip or fall.

   c. If an electrical appliance isn't working, feels hot, or smells hot, tell a teacher right away.

3. **disposing of materials and supplies.**

    a. Generally, liquid household chemicals can be poured into a sink. Completely wash the chemical down the drain with plenty of water.

    b. Generally, solid household chemicals can be placed in a trash can.

    c. Any liquids or solids that **should not** be poured down the sink or placed in the trash have special disposal guidelines. Follow your teacher's instructions.

    d. If glass breaks, do not use your bare hands to pick up the pieces. Use a dustpan and a brush to clean up. "Sharps" trash (trash that has pieces of glass) should be well labeled. The best way to throw away broken glass is to seal it in a labeled cardboard box.

4. **you are concerned about your safety or the safety of others.**

    a. Talk to your teacher immediately. Here are some examples:

       • You smell chemical or gas fumes. This might indicate a chemical or gas leak.

       • You smell something burning.

       • You injure yourself or see someone else who is injured.

       • You are having trouble using your equipment.

       • You do not understand the instructions for the Investigation.

    b. Listen carefully to your teacher's instructions.

    c. Follow your teacher's instructions exactly.

Safety quiz

1. Draw a diagram of your science lab in the space below. Include in your diagram the following items. Include notes that explain how to use these important safety items.

   - Exit/entrance ways
   - Fire extinguisher(s)
   - Fire blanket

   - Eye wash and shower
   - First aid kit
   - Location of eye goggles and lab aprons

   - Sink
   - Trash cans
   - Location of special safety instructions

2. How many fire extinguishers are in your science lab? Explain how to use them.

   _____

   _____

3. List the steps that your teacher and your class would take to safely exit the science lab and the building in case of a fire or other emergency.

   _____

   _____

   _____

4. Before beginning certain Investigations, why should you first put on protective goggles and clothing?

_____

_____

_____

5. Why is teamwork important when you are working in a science lab?

_____

_____

_____

_____

6. Why should you clean up after every Investigation?

_____

_____

_____

7. List at least three things you should you do if you sense danger or see an emergency in your classroom or lab.

_____

_____

_____

_____

8. Five lab situations are described below. What would you do in each situation?
   a. You accidentally knock over a glass container and it breaks on the floor.

_____

_____

_____

   b. You accidentally spill a large amount of water on the floor.

_____

_____

_____

c. You suddenly you begin to smell a "chemical" odor that gives you a headache.

_____

_____

_____

d. You hear the fire alarm while you are working in the lab. You are wearing your goggles and lab apron.

_____

_____

_____

e. While your lab partner has her lab goggles off, she gets some liquid from the experiment in her eye.

_____

_____

_____

f. A fire starts in the lab.

_____

_____

_____

Safety in the science lab is everyone's responsibility!

4 ◤ Safety contract

Keep this contract in your notebook at all times.

By signing it, you agree to follow all the steps necessary to be safe in your science class and lab.

I, _____, (Your name)

☑ Have learned about the use and location of the following:
  - Aprons, gloves
  - Eye protection
  - Eyewash fountain
  - Fire extinguisher and fire blanket
  - First aid kit
  - Heat sources (burners, hot plate, etc) and how to use them safely
  - Waste-disposal containers for glass, chemicals, matches, paper, and wood

☑ Understand the safety information presented.

☑ Will ask questions when I do not understand safety instructions.

☑ Pledge to follow all of the safety guidelines that are presented on the Safety Skill Sheet at all times.

☑ Pledge to follow all of the safety guidelines that are presented on Investigation sheets.

☑ Will always follow the safety instructions that my teacher provides.

Additionally, I pledge to be careful about my own safety and to help others be safe. I understand that I am responsible for helping to create a safe environment in the classroom and lab.

Signed and dated,

_____

Parent's or Guardian's statement:

I have read the Safety Skills sheet and give my consent for the student who has signed the preceding statement to engage in laboratory activities using a variety of equipment and materials, including those described. I pledge my cooperation in urging that she or he observe the safety regulations prescribed.

_____   _____

Signature of Parent or Guardian   Date

Writing a Lab Report

How do you share the results of an experiment?

A lab report is like a story about an experiment. The details in the story help others learn from what you did. A good lab report makes it possible for someone else to repeat your experiment. If their results and conclusions are similar to yours, you have support for your ideas. Through this process we come to understand more about how the world works.

 The parts of a lab report

A lab report follows the steps of the scientific method. Use the checklist below to create your own lab reports:

☐ **Title:** The title makes it easy for readers to quickly identify the topic of your experiment.

☐ **Research question:** The research question tells the reader exactly what you want to find out through your experiment.

☐ **Introduction:** This paragraph describes what you already know about the topic, and shows how this information relates to your experiment.

☐ **Hypothesis:** The hypothesis states the prediction you plan to test in your experiment.

☐ **Materials:** List all the materials you need to do the experiment.

☐ **Procedure:** Describe the steps involved in your experiment. Make sure that you provide enough detail so readers can repeat what you did. You may want to provide sketches of the lab setup. Be sure to name the experimental variable and tell which variables you controlled.

☐ **Data/Observations:** This is where you record what happened, using descriptive words, data tables, and graphs.

☐ **Analysis:** In this section, describe your data in words. Here's a good way to start: *My data shows that...*

☐ **Conclusion:** This paragraph states whether your hypothesis was correct or incorrect. It may suggest a new research question or a new hypothesis.

 A sample lab report

Use the sample lab report on the next two pages as a guide for writing your own lab reports. Remember that you are telling a story about something you did so that others can repeat your experiment.

Name: Jon G.   **Date:** October 20, 2006

Title: The effect of temperature on tomato seedling growth

Research question: Will tomato seedlings grow faster in a warmer environment?

Introduction:

I planted sunflower seeds in my garden on May 1 last year. We had a heat wave the third week of May with temperatures averaging 5°C higher than normal. The seedlings seemed to grow like crazy that week. Next spring, I want to plant tomatoes in my garden. Since tomatoes have to be started indoors in our climate, I am going to test the growth rate of tomato seeds at 20°C and 25°C.

Hypothesis: The seedlings kept at 25°C will grow faster than those kept at 20°C.

Materials:

5-pound bag "starter mix" potting soil	1 packet tomato seeds (at least 50 seeds)
tap water	2 "grow-lights"
5 gallon bucket for mixing soil	plant mister
50 10-centimeter diameter plastic pots	graduated cylinder to measure 20 mL water

Procedure:

1. I mixed a 5-pound bag of "starter mix" potting soil with enough water to make it evenly moist, but not soggy.
2. I filled 50 10-centimeter diameter plastic pots with the moist potting soil. The soil has time release plant food in it.
3. I placed one tomato seed into each pot at a depth of about 3 millimeters.
4. I placed all pots under a "grow-light" in a spare room in our house. I kept the shades closed so that the plants would all receive the same amount of light. The thermostat in this room is set at 25°C.
5. The soil in each pot received five sprays with a plant mister (20 mL) each day to keep it moist.
6. After the seeds germinated, I chose 30 plants that were the same height— 7 millimeters tall. Each of the chosen plants had just two leaves.
7. I divided these plants into two groups. The fifteen plants in group one were left in the spare room, where the temperature remained 25°C.
8. I brought the fifteen plants in group 2 down to our basement. The temperature there is about 5°C cooler than the rooms upstairs. It remains at about 20°C (plus or minus 0.5°C). I set up a second "grow light" just like the first one. There are no windows in the basement so the plants didn't receive any additional light.
9. I continued to give each plant 20 milliliters of water each day for 28 days.
10. I measured the height of all plants on day 7, day 14, day 21, and day 28.

Data/Observations:

Table 1: Temperature change in water and air

Elapsed time (days)	Group 1 (25°C) average plant height (mm)	Group 2 (20°C) Average plant height (mm)
0 (start)	7	7
7	9	7
14	19	12
21	40	23
28	50	29

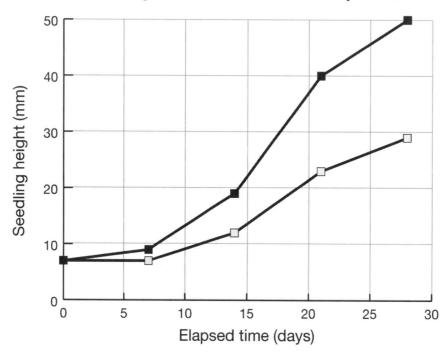

Seedling Growth at Different Temperatures

Analysis:

My data shows that the seedlings in the 25°C environment grew faster than those in the 20°C environment. By the 28th day, the seedlings in the warmer room had grown 43 millimeters, while those in the colder room had grown only 22 millimeters.

Conclusion:

The seedlings in the warmer environment grew almost twice as fast! Next, I would like to test the growth rate of tomato seedlings at 30°C and 35°C. I would like to know how warm is too warm. This would help me determine the best temperature for starting tomato seeds.

Measuring Length

How do you find the length of an object?

Size matters! When you describe the length of an object, or the distance between two objects, you are describing something very important about the object. Is it as small as a bacteria (2 micrometers)? Is it a light year away (9.46×10^{15} meters)? By using the metric system you can quickly see the difference in size between objects.

Materials
- Metric ruler
- Pencil
- Paper
- Small objects
- Calculator

 Reading the meter scale correctly

Look at the ruler in the picture above. Each small line on the top of the ruler represents one millimeter. Larger lines stand for 5 millimeter and 10 millimeter intervals. When the object you are measuring falls between the lines, read the number to the nearest 0.5 millimeter. Practice measuring several objects with your own metric ruler. Compare your results with a lab partner.

2 Stop and think

a. You may have seen a ruler like this marked in centimeter units. How many millimeters are in one centimeter?

_____

_____

_____

b. Notice that the ruler also has markings for reading the English system. Give an example of when it would be better to measure with the English system than the metric system. Give a different example of when it would be better to use the metric system.

_____

_____

_____

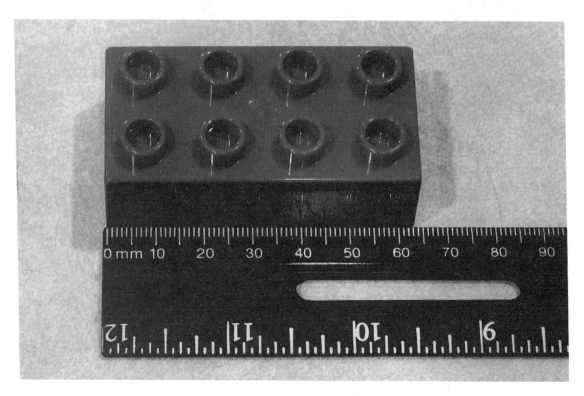

Look at the picture above. How long is the building block?

1. Report the length of the building block to the nearest 0.5 millimeters.
2. Convert your answer to centimeters.
3. Convert your answer to meters.

_____

_____

_____

_____

_____

_____

_____

_____

_____

_____

_____

_____

Example 2: Measuring objects correctly

Look at the picture above. How long is the pencil?

1. Report the length of the pencil to the nearest 0.5 millimeters.
2. Challenge: How many building blocks in example 1 will it take to equal the length of the pencil?
3. Challenge: Convert the length of the pencil to inches by dividing your answer by 25.4 millimeters per inch.

 Example 3: Measuring objects correctly

Look at the picture above. How long is the domino?

1. Report the length of the domino to the nearest 0.5 millimeters.
2. Challenge: How many dominoes will fit end to end on the 30 cm ruler?

6 Practice converting units for length

By completing the examples above you show that you are familiar with some of the prefixes used in the metric system like milli- and centi-. The table below gives other prefixes you may be less familiar with. Try converting the length of the domino from millimeters into all the other units given in the table.

Refer to the multiplication factor this way:

- 1 kilometer equals 1000 meters.

- 1000 millimeters equals 1 meter.

1. How many millimeters are in a kilometer?

| 1000 millimeters per meter × 1000 meters per kilometer = 1,000,000 millimeters per kilometer |

2. Fill in the table with your multiplication factor by converting millimeters to the unit given. The first one is done for you.

| 1000 millimeters per meter × 10^{-12} meters per picometer = 10^{-9} millimeters per picometer |

3. Divide the domino's length in millimeters by the number in your multiplication factor column. This is the answer you will put in the last column.

Prefix	Symbol	Multiplication factor	Scientific notation in meters	Your multiplication factor	Your domino length in:
pico-	p	0.000000000001	10^{-12}	10^{-9}	pm
nano-	n	0.000000001	10^{-9}		nm
micro-	μ	0.000001	10^{-6}		μm
milli	m	0.001	10^{-3}		mm
centi-	c	0.01	10^{-2}		cm
deci-	d	0.1	10^{-1}		dm
deka-	da	10	10^{1}		dam
hecto-	h	100	10^{2}		hm
kilo-	k	1000	10^{3}		km

Measuring Temperature

How do you find the temperature of a substance?

There are many different kinds of thermometers used to measure temperature. Can you think of some you find at home? In your classroom you will use a glass immersion thermometer to find the temperature of a liquid. The thermometer contains alcohol with a red dye in it so you can see the alcohol level inside the thermometer. The alcohol level changes depending on the surrounding temperature. You will practice reading the scale on the thermometer and report your readings in degrees Celsius.

Materials
- Alcohol immersion thermometer
- Beakers
- Water at different temperatures
- Ice

Safety: Glass thermometers are breakable. Handle them carefully. Overheating the thermometer can cause the alcohol to separate and give incorrect readings. Glass thermometers should be stored horizontally or vertically (never upside down) to prevent alcohol from separating.

 Reading the temperature scale correctly

Look at the picture at right. See the close-up of the line inside the thermometer on the scale. The tens scale numbers are given. The ones scale appears as lines. Each small line equals 1 degree Celsius. Practice reading the scale from the bottom to the top. One small line above 20°C is read as 21°C. When the level of the alcohol is between two small lines on the scale, report the number to the nearest 0.5°C.

 Stop and think

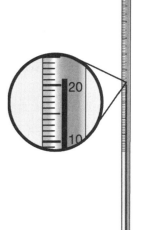

   a. What number does the large line between 20°C and 30°C equal? Figure out by counting the number of small lines between 20°C and 30°C.

   b. Give the temperature of the thermometer in the picture above.

   c. Practice rounding the following temperature values to the nearest 0.5°C: 23.1°C, 29.8°C, 30.0°C, 31.6°C, 31.4°C.

   d. Water at 0°C and 100°C has different properties. Describe what water looks like at these temperatures.

   e. What will happen to the level of the alcohol if you hold the thermometer by the bulb?

Reading the temperature of water in a beaker

An immersion thermometer must be placed in liquid up to the solid line on the thermometer (at least 2 and one half inches of liquid). Wait about 3 minutes for the temperature of the thermometer to equal the temperature of the liquid. Record the temperature to the nearest 0.5°C when the level stops moving.

1.   Place the thermometer in the beaker. Check to make sure that the water level is above the solid line on the thermometer.

2.   Wait until the alcohol level stops moving (about three minutes). Record the temperature to the nearest 0.5°C.

 ### Reading the temperature of warm water in a beaker

A warm liquid will cool to room temperature. For a warm liquid, record the warmest temperature you observe before the temperature begins to decrease.

1.   Repeat the procedure above with a beaker of warm (not boiling) water.

2.   Take temperature readings every 30 seconds. Record the warmest temperature you observe.

 ### Reading the temperature of ice water in a beaker

When a large amount of ice is added to water, the temperature of the water will drop until the ice and water are the same temperature. After the ice has melted, the cold water will warm to room temperature.

1.   Repeat the procedure above with a beaker of ice and water.

2.   Take temperature readings every 30 seconds. Record the coldest temperature you observe.

Calculating Volume

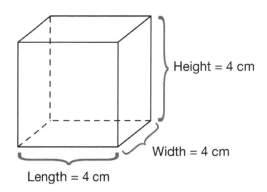
How do you find the volume of a three dimensional shape?

Volume is the amount of space an object takes up. If you know the dimensions of a solid object, you can find the object's volume. A two dimensional shape has length and width. A three dimensional object has length, width, and height. This investigation will give you practice finding volume for different solid objects.

Materials
- Pencil
- Calculator

 Calculating volume of a cube

A cube is a geometric solid that has length, width and height. If you measure the sides of a cube, you will find that all the edges have the same measurement. The volume of a cube is found by multiplying the length times width times height. In the picture each side is 4 centimeters so the problem looks like this:

$$V = l \times w \times h$$

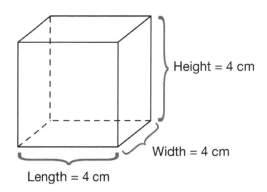

Height = 4 cm

Width = 4 cm

Length = 4 cm

Example:

Volume = 4 centimeters × 4 centimeters × 4 centimeters = 64 centimeters^3

 Stop and think

a. What are the units for volume in the example above?

b. In the example above, if the edge of the cube is 4 inches, what will the volume be? Give the units.

c. How is finding volume different from finding area?

d. If you had cubes with a length of 1 centimeter, how many would you need to build the cube in the picture above?

3 ◣ Calculating volume of a rectangular prism

Rectangular prisms are like cubes, except not all of the sides are equal. A shoebox is a rectangular prism. You can find the volume of a rectangular prism using the same formula given above $V = l \times w \times h$.

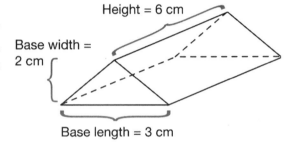
Height = 2 cm
Length = 8 cm
Width = 3 cm

Another way to say it is to multiply the area of the base times the height.

1. Find the area of the base for the rectangular prism pictured above.

2. Multiply the area of the base times the height. Record the volume of the rectangular prism.

3. PRACTICE: Find the volume for a rectangular prism with a height 6 cm, length 5 cm, and width 3 cm. Be sure to include the units in all of your answers.

4 ◣ Calculating volume for a triangular prism

Triangular prisms have three sides and two triangular bases. The volume of the triangular prism is found by multiplying the area of the base times the height. The base is a triangle.

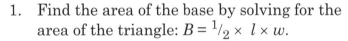
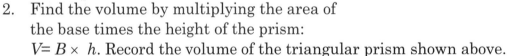
Height = 6 cm
Base width = 2 cm
Base length = 3 cm

1. Find the area of the base by solving for the area of the triangle: $B = \frac{1}{2} \times l \times w$.

2. Find the volume by multiplying the area of the base times the height of the prism: $V = B \times h$. Record the volume of the triangular prism shown above.

3. PRACTICE: Find the volume of the triangular prism with a height 10 cm, triangular base width 4 cm, and triangular base length 5 cm.

5 ◣ Calculating volume for a cylinder

A soup can is a cylinder. A cylinder has two circular bases and a round surface. The volume of the cylinder is found by multiplying the area of the base times the height. The base is a circle.

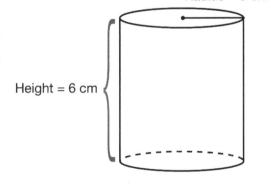
Radius = 3 cm
Height = 6 cm

1. Find the area of the base by solving for the area of a circle: $A = \pi \times r^2$.

2. Find the volume by multiplying the area of the base times the height of the cylinder: $V = A \times h$. Record the volume of the cylinder shown above.

3. PRACTICE: Find the volume of the cylinder with height 8 cm and radius 4 cm.

6 Calculating volume for a cone

An ice cream cone really is a cone! A cone has height and a circular base. The volume of the cone is found by multiplying $^1/_2$ times the area of the base times the height.

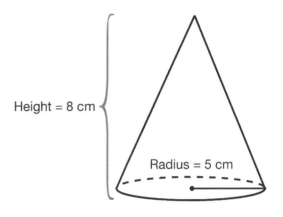

Height = 8 cm

Radius = 5 cm

1. Find the area of the base by solving for the area of a circle: $A = \pi \times r^2$.

2. Find the volume by multiplying? times the area of the base times the height: $V = ^1/_2 \times A \times h$. Record the volume of the cone shown above.

3. PRACTICE: Find the volume of the cone with height 8 cm and radius 4 cm. Contrast your answer with the volume you found for the cylinder with the same dimensions. What is the difference in volume? Does this make sense?

7 Calculating the volume for a rectangular pyramid

A pyramid looks like a cone. It has height and a rectangular base. The volume of the rectangular pyramid is found by multiplying $^1/_2$ times the area of the base times the height.

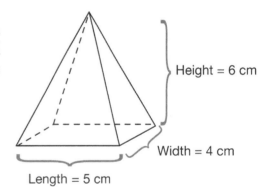

Height = 6 cm

Width = 4 cm

Length = 5 cm

1. Find the area of the base by multiplying the length times the width: $A = l \times w$.

2. Find the volume by multiplying $^1/_3$ times the area of the base times the height: $V = ^1/_3 \times A \times h$. Record the volume of the rectangular pyramid shown above.

3. PRACTICE: Find the volume of a rectangular pyramid with height 10 cm and width 4 cm and length 5 cm.

4. EXTRA CHALLENGE: If a rectangular pyramid had a height of 8 cm and a width of 4 cm, what length would it need to have to give the same volume as the cone in practice question 4 above?

8 ◣ Calculating volume for a triangular pyramid

A triangular pyramid is like a rectangular pyramid, but its base is a triangle. Find the area of the base first. Then calculate the volume by multiplying $^1/_3$ times the area of the base times the height.

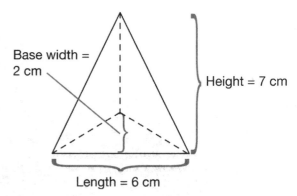

1. Find the area of the base by solving for the area of a triangle: $B = ^1/_2 \times l \times w$.

2. Find the volume by multiplying $^1/_3$ times the area of the base times the height: $V = ^1/_3 \times A \times h$. Find the volume of the triangular pyramid shown above.

3. PRACTICE: Find the volume of the triangular pyramid with height 10 cm and width 6 cm and length 5 cm.

9 ◣ Calculating volume for a sphere

To find the volume of a sphere, you only need to know one dimension about the sphere, its radius.

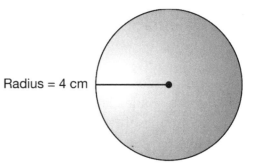

1. Find the volume of a sphere: $V = ^4/_3 \pi r^3$. Find the volume for the sphere shown above.

2. PRACTICE: Find the volume for a sphere with radius 2 cm.

3. EXTRA CHALLENGE: Find the volume for a sphere with diameter 10 cm.

Measuring Volume

How do you find the volume of an irregular object?

It's easy to find the volume of a shoebox or a basketball. You just take a few measurements, plug the numbers into a math formula, and you have figured it out. But what if you want to find the volume of a bumpy rock, or an acorn, or a house key? There aren't any simple math formulas to help you out. However, there's an easy way to find the volume of an irregular object, as long the object is waterproof!

Materials

- Displacement tank
- Water source
- Disposable cup
- Beaker
- Graduated cylinder
- Sponges or paper towel
- Object to be measured

 Setting up the displacement tank

Set the displacement tank on a level surface. Place a disposable cup under the tank's spout. Carefully fill the tank until the water begins to drip out of the spout. When the water stops flowing, discard the water collected in the disposable cup. Set the cup aside and place a beaker under the spout.

 Stop and think

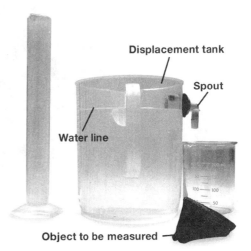

Displacement tank

Spout

Water line

Object to be measured

   a. What do you think will happen when you place an object into the tank?

   b. Which object would cause more water to come out of the spout, an acorn or a fist-sized rock?

   c. Why are we interested in how much water comes out of the spout?

   d. Explain how the displacement tank measures volume.

 Measuring volume with the displacement tank

1. Gently place a waterproof object into the displacement tank. It is important to avoid splashing the water or creating a wave that causes extra water to flow out of the spout. It may take a little practice to master this step.

2. When the water stops flowing out of the spout, it can be poured from the beaker into a graduated cylinder for precise measurement. The volume of the water displaced is equal to the object's volume.
Note: Occasionally, when a small object is placed in the tank, no water will flow out. This happens because an air bubble has formed in the spout. Simply tap the spout with a pencil to release the air bubble.

3. If you wish to measure the volume of another object, don't forget to refill the tank with water first!

Measuring Mass with a Triple Beam Balance

How do you find the mass of an object?

Why can't you use a bathroom scale to measure the mass of a paperclip? You could if you were finding the mass of a lot of them at one time! To find the mass of objects less than a kilogram you will need to use the triple beam balance.

 Parts of the triple beam balance

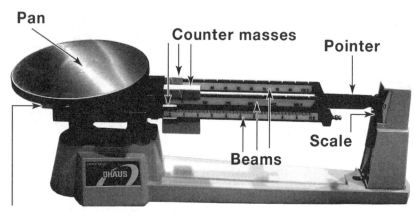

2 Setting up and zeroing the balance

The triple beam balance works like a see-saw. When the mass of your object is perfectly balanced by the counter masses on the beam, the pointer will rest at 0. Add up the readings on the three beams to find the mass of your object. The unit of measure for this triple beam balance is grams.

1. Place the balance on a level surface.

2. Clean any objects or dust off the pan.

3. Move all counter masses to 0. The pointer should rest at 0. Use the adjustment screw to adjust the pointer to 0, if necessary. When the pointer rests at 0 with no objects on the pan, the balance is said to be zeroed.

Finding a known mass

You can check that the triple beam balance is working correctly by using a mass set. Your teacher will provide the correct mass value for these objects.

1. After zeroing the balance, place an object with a known mass on the pan.

2. Move the counter masses to the right one at a time from largest to smallest. When the pointer is resting at 0 the numbers under the three counter masses should add up to the known mass.

3. If the pointer is above or below 0, recheck the balance set up. Recheck the position of the counter masses. Counter masses must be properly seated in a groove. Check with your teacher to make sure you are getting the correct mass before finding the mass an unknown object.

Finding the mass of an unknown object

1. After zeroing the balance, place an object with an unknown mass on the pan. Do not place hot objects or chemicals directly on the pan

2. Move the largest counter mass first. Place it in the first notch after zero. Wait until the pointer stops moving. If the pointer is above 0, move the counter mass to the next notch. Continue to move the counter mass to the right, one notch at a time until the pointer is slightly above 0. Go to step 3. If the pointer is below 0, move the counter mass back one notch. When the pointer rests at 0, you do not need to move any more counter masses.

3. Move the next largest counter mass from 0 to the first notch. Watch to see where the pointer rests. If it rests above 0, move the counter mass to the next notch. Repeat until the point rests at 0, or slightly above. If the pointer is slightly above 0, go to step 4.

4. Move the smallest counter mass from 0 to the position on the beam where the pointer rests at 0.

5. Add the masses from the three beams to get the mass of the unknown object. You should be able to record a number for the hundreds place, the tens place, the ones place, and the tenths place and the hundredths place. The hundredths place can be read to 0.00 or 0.05. You may have zeros in your answer.

5 ▶ Reading the balance correctly

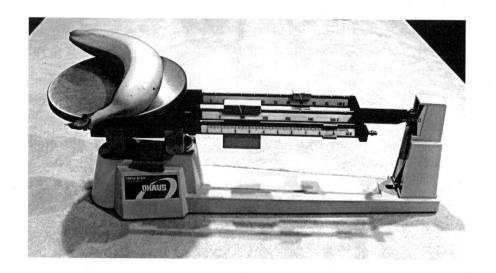

Look at the picture above. To find the mass of the object, locate the counter mass on each beam. Read the numbers directly below each counter mass. You can read the smallest mass to 0.05 grams. Write down the three numbers. Add them together. Report your answer in grams. Does your answer agree with others? If not, check your mass values from each beam to find your mistake.

6 ▶ Finding the mass of an object in a container

To measure the mass of a liquid or powder you will need an empty container on the pan to hold the sample. You must find the mass of the empty container first. After you place the object in the container and find the total mass, you can subtract the container's mass from the total to find the object's mass.

1. After zeroing the balance, place a beaker on the pan.

2. Follow directions for finding the mass of an unknown object. Record the mass of the beaker.

3. Place a small object in the beaker.

4. Move the counter masses to the right, largest to smallest, to find the total mass.

5. Subtract the beaker's mass from the total mass. This is the mass of your object in grams.

Using a Compound Microscope

How do you use a compound microscope to see objects?

Have you ever used a magnifying glass? Objects under the magnifying glass look larger than real life. A compound microscope is like a magnifying glass that uses more than one lens to magnify small objects. In this investigation you will become familiar with the parts of the compound microscope. Then you will examine a specimen with microscope and practice using different levels of magnification.

Materials
- Compound microscope
- Power supply
- Clean glass slides
- Permanent markers
- Prepared specimens on glass slides
- Lens paper

 Identifying the parts of the microscope

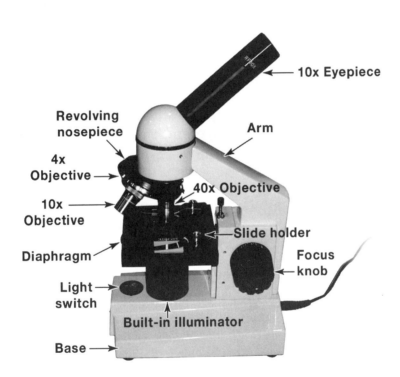

Look at the picture above. Each of the parts of the microscope is labeled. The major parts of the microscope are the light source, the specimen stage, the eye piece, and the objective lenses. You will find a description of the microscope parts at the end of this write up.

Care of the microscope

Microscopes are expensive pieces of equipment containing glass parts that can break or scratch easily. Never touch the glass with your fingers.

1. Always carry the microscope with two hands. Hold the arm of the microscope with one hand and support the base with the other hand. Never turn the microscope upside down or the eyepiece could fall out.

2. Place the microscope on a level surface.

3. Check to make sure the battery operated built-in illuminator is working. The microscope comes with a battery charger that can be plugged into an electrical outlet, if needed.

4. Without removing them, inspect the objectives, eyepiece, and illuminator for dust. If necessary, wipe the glass surfaces with lens paper. Store the microscope with a dust cover to keep it clean.

5. When you are finished using the microscope, switch to the lowest power objective (4x), lower the stage, switch off the power, cover the microscope with a dust cover, and return the microscope to its storage area.

 Setting up the microscope

The microscope allows you to look in the eyepiece and see an image of the object on the stage. There are some differences between the image and the object. By following these directions, you will see how the image is different from the object.

1. With your teacher's permission write a small letter "e" on a glass slide with a permanent marker.

2. Turn on the built-in illuminator.

3. Place the slide on the stage with the letter "e" facing you. Secure the slide under the slide holders.

4. Lower the stage until it is about half way between the built-in illuminator and the objective.

5. Move the revolving nosepiece slowly until the 4x objective is clicked into place and directly above the object.

6. Look into the eyepiece. Adjust the focus knob until the image appears in focus.

7. Carefully move the slide until the image in centered. Focus again if necessary. What do notice about the direction of the letter "e"?

8. What happens to the image when you move the slide to the right? To the left? Forward? Backward? Specimens appear reversed when you look at them under the microscope because a mirror is used inside the microscope to direct the light rays to the eyepiece.

Adjusting the microscope

The microscope is adjustable so you can look at different types of samples. The following directions explain the adjustments you can make to get the best images possible.

1. Use the focus knob to move the stage up and down to see your specimen more clearly. The stage should be lowered when you are putting a slide on or off the stage.

2. Change the objective you are using by rotating the revolving nosepiece until a new objective clicks into place directly above the slide. An objective with a larger number increases the size of the image. Each objective has its magnifying power stamped on it.

    a. Find the 4x, the 10x, and the 40x objectives.

    b. Always start with the 4x objective directly above the slide when looking at a sample for the first time. View the sample through the eyepiece and bring it into focus.

    c. Center the object by moving the slide with your hand before changing the objective.

    d. Objectives are said to be parfocal if you can change from one objective to another without having to refocus the image very much. See if your image appears in focus when you switch to the 10x objective.

    e. Using a 10x objective and a 10x eyepiece the object appears one hundred times larger than its actual size. This number is called the total magnification. To solve for the total magnification, multiply the number on the objective times the number on the eyepiece. Solve for the total magnification for a 4x objective and a 10x eyepiece. Repeat the calculation using the 40x objective and the 10x eyepiece.

    f. After increasing the magnification, you will notice two things about the image. The image may appear darker, and the field of view becomes smaller. Objects near the edge of the image may disappear when you switch to a higher magnification. If your specimen is no longer visible, center the image at low magnification before switching to a higher magnification. These two effects are the normal result of switching to a higher magnification.

    g. Rotate the nosepiece slowly to move the 40x objective in place. Watch the microscope from the side while you do this. The 40x objective is very close to the stage when it is used correctly. The 40x objective is spring-loaded and retractable to prevent damage to the objective and slide in most cases. View your specimen through the eyepiece and adjust the focus if necessary.

    h. At higher magnification the amount of light entering the objective decreases. To increase the amount of light passing through the specimen, rotate the diaphragm under the stage. Select one of six different size holes to control the amount of light passing through.

◣5 Examining specimens under a microscope

Your teacher will provide you with prepared specimens on slides. In some cases, a stain has been used to allow you to see the specimen better. Follow the steps below to set up the microscope and record your observations.

1. Lower the stage until it is about half way between the built-in illuminator and the objective.

2. Turn on the built-in illuminator.

3. Place the slide on the stage and secure it with the slide holders.

4. Move the revolving nosepiece slowly until the 4x objective clicks into place and is directly above the object.

5. Look into the eyepiece. Bring the slide into focus using the focus knob.

6. Make a detailed sketch of what you see in the space below. Record your specimen name and your observations

7. Use the 10x objective and repeat steps 5 and 6.

8. Use the 40x objective and repeat steps 5 and 6.

Specimen: _____
(Low power)

Specimen: _____
(Medium power)

Specimen: _____
(Highpower)

Observations:

_____

_____

Observations:

_____

_____

Observations:

_____

_____

- **10x Eyepiece**: One (monocular) or two (binocular) lenses that you look through to see the image
- **Built-in pointer:** A pointer inside the eyepiece to help you center your image
- **Arm:** Supports the upper half of the microscope
- **4x Objective:** Low power scanning objective
- **10x Objective:** Medium power objective
- **40x Objective:** High power objective
- **Revolving nosepiece:** Can be rotated to change objectives
- **Stage:** The platform for holding the slide
- **Focus knob:** The knob that adjusts the height of the stage
- **Specimen:** Sample to be observed on the slide
- **Slide:** Glass support for specimens
- **Cover slip:** Glass cover for specimens
- **Light switch:** Switch to turn on built-in illuminator
- **Built-in illuminator:** Light source required to view specimens
- **Base:** Supports entire microscope
- **Power cord:** For recharging batteries to illuminator
- **Slide holder:** Clips to hold slide to stage
- **Diaphragm:** Adjusts amount of light entering specimen

Recording Observations in the Lab

How do you record valid observations for an experiment in the lab?

When you perform an experiment you will be making important observations. You and others will use these observations to test a hypothesis. In order for an experiment to be valid, the evidence you collect must be objective and repeatable. This investigation will give you practice making and recording good observations.

> **Materials**
> - Paper
> - Pencil
> - Calculator
> - Ruler

 Making valid observations

Valid scientific observations are objective and repeatable. Scientific observations are limited to one's senses and the equipment used to make these observations. An objective observation means that the observer describes only what happened. The observer uses data, words, and pictures to describe the observations as exactly as possible. An experiment is repeatable if other scientists can see or repeat the same result. The following exercise gives you practice identifying good scientific observations.

 Exercise 1

1. **Which observation is the most objective? Circle the correct letter.**
   a. My frog died after 3 days in the aquarium. I miss him.
   b. The frog died after 3 days in the aquarium. We will test the temperature and water conditions to find out why.
   c. Frogs tend to die in captivity. Ours did after three days.

2. **Which observation is the most descriptive? Circle the correct letter.**
   a. After weighing 3.000 grams of sodium bicarbonate into an Erlenmeyer flask, we slowly added 50.0 milliliters of vinegar. The contents of the flask began to bubble.
   b. We weighed the powder into a glass container. We added acid. It bubbled a lot.
   c. We saw a fizzy reaction.

3. **Which experiment has enough detail to repeat? Circle the correct letter.**

    a. Each student took a swab culture from his or her teeth. The swab was streaked onto nutrient agar plates and incubated at 37 C.

    b. Each student received a nutrient agar plate and a swab. Each student performed a swab culture of his or her teeth. The swab was streaked onto the agar plate. The plates were stored face down in the 37 C incubator and checked daily for growth. After 48 hours the plates were removed from the incubator and each student recorded his or her results.

    c. Each student received a nutrient agar plate and a swab. Each student performed a swab culture of his or her teeth. The swab was streaked onto the agar plate. The plates were stored face down in the 37 C incubator and checked daily for growth. After 48 hours the plates were removed from the incubator and each student counted the number of colonies present on the surface of the agar.

 Recording valid observations

As a part of your investigations you will be asked to record observations on a skill sheet or in the results section of a lab report. There are different ways to show your observations. Here are some examples:

1. **Short description:** Use descriptive words to explain what you did or saw. Write complete sentences. Give as much detail as possible about the experiment. Try to answer the following questions: What? Where? When? Why? and How?

2. **Tables:** Tables are a good way to display the data you have collected. Later, the data can be plotted on a graph. Be sure to include a title for the table, labels for the sets of data, and units for the values. Check values to make sure you have the correct number of significant figures.

Table I: U.S. penny mass by year

Year manufactured	1977	1978	1979	1980	1981	1982	1983	1984	1985
Mass (grams)	3.0845	3.0921	3.0689	2.9915	3.0023	2.5188	2.5042	2.4883	2.5230

3. **Graphs and charts:** A graph or chart is a picture of your data. There are different kinds of graphs and charts: line graphs, trend charts, bar graphs, and pie graphs, for example. A line graph is shown below.

Label the important parts of your graph. Give your graph a title. The x-axis and y-axis should have labels for the data, the unit values, and the number range on the graph.

The line graph in the example has a straight line through the data. Sometimes data does not fit a straight line. Often scientists will plot data first in a trend chart to see how the data looks. Check with your instructor if you are unsure how to display your data.

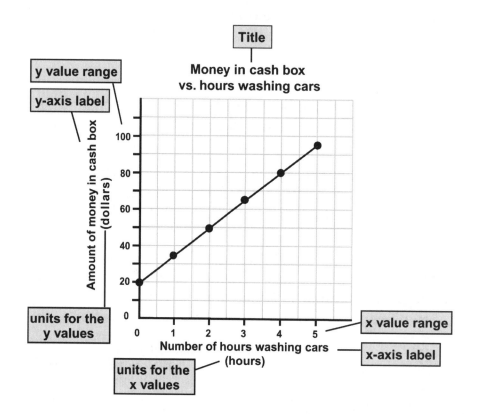

4. **Drawings:** Sometimes you will record observations by drawing a sketch of what you see. The example below was observed under a microscope.

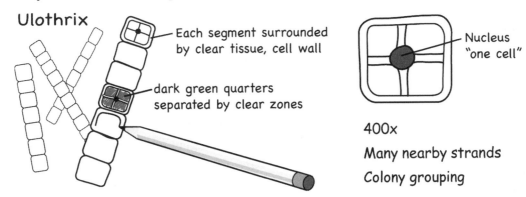

Give the name of the specimen. Draw enough detail to make the sketch look realistic. Use color, when possible. Identify parts of the object you were asked to observe. Provide the magnification or size of the image.

4 ▸ Exercise 2: Practice recording valid observations

A lab report form has been given to you by your instructor. This exercise gives you a chance to read through an experiment and fill in information in the appropriate sections of the lab report form. Use this opportunity to practice writing and graphing scientific observations. Then answer the following questions about the experiment.

A student notices that when he presses several pennies in a pressed penny machine, his brand new penny has some copper color missing and he can see silver-like material underneath. He wonders, "Are some pennies made differently than others?" The student has a theory that not all U.S. pennies are made the same. He thinks that if pennies are made differently now he might be able to find out when the change occurred. He decides to collect a U.S. penny for each year from 1977 to the present, record the date, and take its mass. The student records the data in a table and creates a graph plotting U.S. penny mass vs. year. Below is a table of some of his data:

Table 2: U.S. penny mass by year

Year manufactured	1977	1978	1979	1980	1981	1982	1983	1984	1985
Mass (grams)	3.0845	3.0921	3.0689	2.9915	3.0023	2.5188	2.5042	2.4883	2.5230

5 ▸ Stop and think

a. What observation did the student make first before he began his experiment?

b. How did the student display his observations?

c. In what section of the lab report did you show observations?

d. What method did you use to display the observations? Explain why you chose this one.

Marble Launcher

You will need:

- Marble launcher
- Hex wrench
- Black plastic marble
- 2 Hex screws

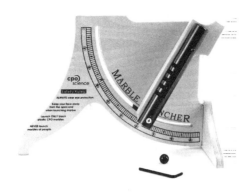

1.

Identifying the parts of the marble launcher

The marble launcher will come with six pieces; the base, the main assembly, a small black marble, two small hex nuts, and a small hex wrench.

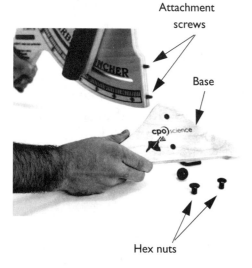

2.

Setting up the marble launcher

The marble launcher itself has two parts; the base and the main assembly. These two parts attach together with hex nuts that fit onto attachment screws that are embedded into the bottom of the main assembly. Line up the two holes in the base with the attachment screws on the main assembly.

3.

Attaching the base

The hex nuts fit onto the attachment screws through the holes in the base. Use the small hex wrench to tighten both until snug.

4.   Loading the marble

Set launcher to desired angle before loading the marble. To load, put the marble right into the hole at the top of the barrel. **Be sure to load the marble into the barrel before pulling the launch lever back into the locked and ready to fire position.**

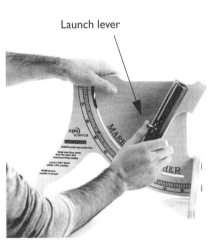

Launch lever

5.   Launching the marble

After loading the marble into the barrel pull the launch lever back to one of the five possible notches and set into place. The marble launcher will be ready to launch. Push down on the launch lever gently with your thumb to slowly slide the lever off the notch to send the marble flying.

Light and Optics

You will need:

- Optics table
- LED lamps
- Diffraction grating glasses
- Magnet securing strips

- Power adapter
- Laser
- Polarizing filters
- Large graph paper

- Flat lenses
- Prism
- Mirror/projection screen

1. Parts of the Light & Optics set

The lights & optics set comes with the optics table, a power adapter, three flat lenses, three LED lamps (red, green and blue), a red laser, a prism, diffraction grating glasses, two polarizing filters, a mirror/projection screen, two magnetic securing strips, and large graph paper.

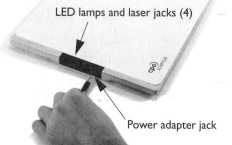

LED lamps and laser jacks (4)

Power adapter jack

2. Attaching the adapter to the optics table

On the side of the optics table there is a series of jacks. Four of them are identical and are used to plug in the LED lights and the laser. One if them is not like the others and it is on the far right of the black plastic plate. Plug the power adapter into this jack, and then plug the other end into a wall outlet.

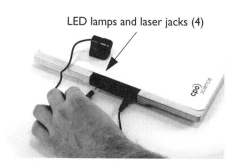

LED lamps and laser jacks (4)

3. Attaching the LED lamps to the optics table

There are four identical jacks on the side of the optics table. You can use any one of these jacks for all three LED lamps or the laser. Plug in one of the lamps to make sure your optics table has power. There is no on/off switch, the light should go on if there is power.

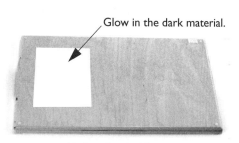

Glow in the dark material.

Underside of table

4. Finding the glow in the dark sticker

On the underside of the optics table there is sticker made out of glow in the dark material. It can be made to glow by exposing it to light, and can be observed to glow in a darkened room.

You will need:

- Physics stand pole
- Physics stand washer
- Physics stand base
- Physics stand bolt

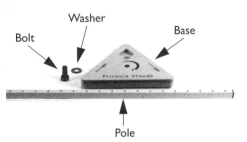

Washer
Bolt
Base
PHYSICS STAND
Pole

1.

Identifying the parts of the physics stand

There are four parts to the physics stand; the base, the pole, the washer and the bolt.

2.

Placing the bolt into the base

From the bottom of the base slide the large bolt through the hole.

3.

Sliding the washer onto the bolt

Be sure to push the bolt into the cut-out triangle on the bottom of the stand. The washer will fit over the threaded part of the bolt.

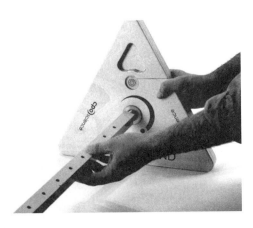

4.

Attaching the pole to the base

The pole screws onto the threads of the bolt. The bolt will not spin when you hold the bolt into the cut-out triangle on the bottom of the base. Spin the pole until it screws down snug onto the washer.

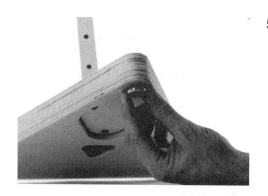

5.

Leveling the stand

There are three adjustable feet on the bottom of the base. These feet screw into the base. They can be extended by unscrewing them a few turns.

Bubble

6.

Using the leveling bubble

When the bubble is directly in the center of the small circle, the stand is level. By adjusting the feet on the bottom of the base by small amounts, the stand can be brought into level.

Ropes and Pulleys

You will need:

- Physics stand assembly
- 1 set of weights
- Tape measure

- Upper and lower pulley blocks attached by red safety string
- 1 set of spring scales
- Blue knob

- Yellow string with cord stops
- Black knob

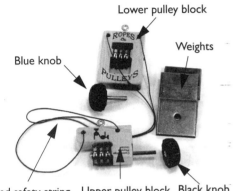

Lower pulley block

Weights

Blue knob

Red safety string   Upper pulley block   Black knob

1.

Identifying the parts of the ropes and pulleys

The ropes and pulleys set is an ideal way to learn the basic principles behind how simple machines work. The upper and lower pulley blocks each contain three pulleys. The number of pulleys through which the string passes can be varied by passing the string through the desired number. The force of the bottom pulley block can be varied by adding or subtracting weights. The pulleys contain low friction bearings for accurate force measurements.

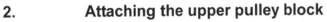

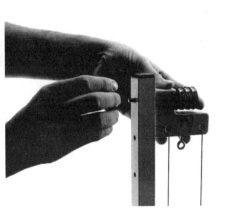

2.

Attaching the upper pulley block

Slide the threaded rod attached to the upper pulley block through the top hole of the physics stand. Secure the pulley block with the black knob. You should now have the upper pulley block secured, while the lower pulley block hangs below on the two red safety strings.

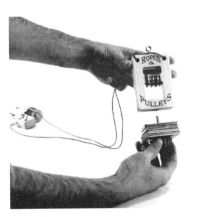

3.

Weighing the bottom block

Add weights to the bottom block using the blue knob with the threaded stud. Slide the threaded stud through the hole in the weight and screw it into the bottom of the lower pulley.

After the weights have been secured, weigh the lower pulley block by hanging it onto a spring scale using the eyelet on top.

4.

Stringing the pulley blocks

The yellow string is the one you will use to move the lower pulley block up and down. The red strings are the safety strings that hold the bottom block while you arrange the yellow strings. The cord stops are used as reference markers for measuring the length of string needed to raise the lower block a given distance.

The first step to stringing the ropes & pulleys is to choose where to connect the brass clip on the end of the yellow string. The clip can either be attached to the upper pulley block or the lower pulley block using the eyelet on either block.

If the string is connected to the lower pulley block a mechanical advantage of 1, 3 or 5 can be obtained (1, 3, or 5 supporting strings). The diagram to the right shows a mechanical advantage of 1.

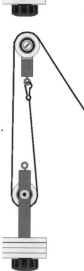

Connect string to the lower pulley block for mechanical advantage of 1,3, or 5.

If the string is connected to the upper pulley block a mechanical advantage of 2, 4, or 6 can be obtained (2, 4, or 6 supporting strings). The diagram to the right shows a mechanical advantage of 2.

Connect string to the upper pulley block for mechanical advantage of 2,4, or 6.

Lever

You will need:

- Physics stand assembly
- 1 set of weights
- 1 set of spring scales
- 1 thumb screw
- Loop strings
- Lever
- 1 black knob

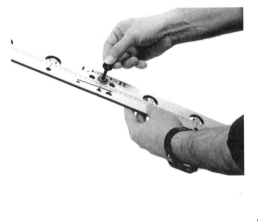

1.

Identifying the parts of the lever

The lever is attached to the stand with a thumb screw and a knob. Loops of string are put through weights and the weights are hung from the lever. Spring scales can be attached to the lever to measure the force created by hanging weights.

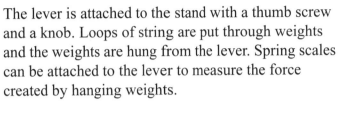

2.

.Place thumb screw through lever

Slide the thumbscrew through a hole in the lever. The screw should be inserted from the side of the lever that has the scale printed on it.

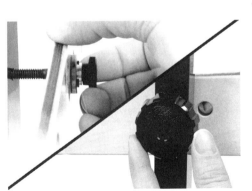

3.

Attaching the lever to the stand

Select the desired hole in the Physics Stand and slide the thumbscrew, with the Lever on it, through the hole. Secure the assembly using the black plastic knob.

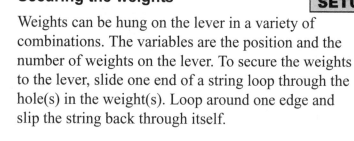

4. **Securing the weights**

Weights can be hung on the lever in a variety of combinations. The variables are the position and the number of weights on the lever. To secure the weights to the lever, slide one end of a string loop through the hole(s) in the weight(s). Loop around one edge and slip the string back through itself.

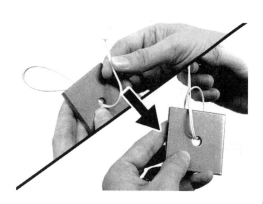

5. **Hanging the weights**

Hang the weight to the lever by placing the loop of string attached to weights securely around one of the mushroom shaped slots. Weights may be hung from more than one location on the lever.

6. **Using the spring scales**

Loop the hook part of a spring scale through one of the holes used to attach weights. Hold spring scale from the top using the metal loop. Slowly lift the scale upward, take a reading while in motion and then slowly lower, also taking a reading. The scale will only need to be lifted and then lowered 3-4 inches for a reading. The true reading will be the average of the two readings.